The Canterbury Tales

General Prologue and Five Most Popular Tales

Geoffrey Chaucer

PRESTWICK HOUSE
LITERARY TOUCHSTONE PRESS

P.O. Box 658 • Clayton, Delaware 19938

SENIOR EDITOR: Paul Moliken

EDITOR: Elizabeth Osborne

COVER CONCEPT/DESIGN: Wendy Smith, Elizabeth Osborne
      Photography: Larry Knox
      Photo props courtesy of: Actors Attic • Costumes • Theatrical Supplies
      www.actorsattic.com

PRODUCTION: Jerry Clark

PRESTWICK HOUSE
LITERARY TOUCHSTONE PRESS

P.O. BOX 658 • CLAYTON, DELAWARE 19938
TEL: 1.800.932.4593
FAX: 1.888.718.9333
WEB: www.prestwickhouse.com

This Prestwick House edition, is a selection of unabridged, but slightly modified tales as they originally appeared in *Canterbury Tales: Rendered into Modern English by J. U. Nicolson,* published in 1934 by Garden City Publishing Company, Inc., New York

ISBN 1-58049-396-3

CONTENTS

Notes

What is a literary classic and why are these classic works important to the world?

A literary classic is a work of the highest excellence that has something important to say about life and/or the human condition and says it with great artistry. A classic, through its enduring presence, has withstood the test of time and is not bound by time, place, or customs. It speaks to us today as forcefully as it spoke to people one hundred or more years ago, and as forcefully as it will speak to people of future generations. For this reason, a classic is said to have universality.

Geoffrey Chaucer was probably born around 1343, in London. His father and grandfather were prosperous wine-traders. As a young man, Geoffrey was able to gain a position in the court of a countess. Later, he became a valet in the court of King Edward III.

In his teens, Chaucer traveled to France during one of the battles of the Hundred Years' War. He was taken prisoner and ransomed by the king himself.

Chaucer traveled to Italy, where he became familiar with the works of the great Italian poets Dante (1265-1341), and Boccaccio (1313-1375). He was also in contact with French poets, whose works he translated.

After his service in the court, Chaucer was given various mid-level positions in the government, including Comptroller of the Port of London. In this role, he oversaw customs regulations on incoming goods. He also went to Flanders (modern-day Holland and Belgium) on a government mission. All of these experiences influenced the *Canterbury Tales*.

Chaucer's other major poem is *Troilus and Criseyde*, a love story of about 8,000 lines; he also wrote several shorter poetic works. He authored a *Treatise on the Astrolabe* (an informative work about an important navigational tool used by sailors) and translated the late Roman philosopher Boethius' *Consolation of Philosophy* into English.

In the year 1400, Chaucer died; he may have been murdered by enemies of King Richard II. Though Europe was already undergoing tremendous change during his lifetime, his death is often used as a marker of the end of the medieval period.

Reading Pointers for Sharper Insights

As you read *Canterbury Tales*, keep the following information in mind:

Historical Circumstances: In the fourteenth century, when Geoffrey Chaucer was writing, England was a wild place. War, plague, church scandal, and political controversy were all raging, and the author of the *Canterbury Tales* was in the middle of all of it.

The Hundred Years' War with France (actually a series of battles, not a continuous war) was in progress; Chaucer himself actually went to France as part of this war, and was personally ransomed by King Edward III.

During the same time period, the Black Death, or bubonic plague, was devastating Europe. The chaos of the plague led to some dishonest behavior (notice how the Physician in the *Tales* made all his money), but, more importantly, it permanently altered the order of European society. Whereas medieval society had generally been divided into three *estates*, or classes (clergy, aristocrat, and commoner), the plague helped form a new category: the middle class. So many workers died that there was a labor shortage; survivors, newly in demand, could lobby for higher wages and better working conditions. Eventually, their improvement in lifestyle became permanent.

The Peasants' Revolt of 1381 took place in response to a harsh tax on these laborers; Chaucer mentions one of the leaders of the Revolt, Jack Straw, in the *Nun's Priest's Tale*. As you read, notice how Chaucer both adheres to the idea of the three estates and departs from it. Which characters are easy to classify, and which seem to belong to more than one class?

The Catholic Church, by far the most important institution in Europe, was also experiencing internal strife. In 1378, a controversy over the papal election resulted in the naming of three popes, all of whom claimed legitimacy. Within England, the theologian John Wycliffe was attacking the doctrine that priests must act as interpreters of God's word, and asserting that each ordinary churchgoer had the power to understand God for himself. Wycliffe's followers, called *Lollards*, were attacked as heretics by the king, and several were beheaded. Can you find any hint of this religious violence in the *Canterbury Tales*?

Structure of the Church: The medieval church divided the clergy into two categories: *regular* and *secular*. The regular clergy were those men, like monks and friars, who belonged to a religious order; they took vows of celibacy and poverty. Monks were supposed to live lives of quiet reflection, prayer and solitude, while friars were supposed to go out into their communities and tend to the people there. Friars were *mendicant*, which means that they owned no property and supported themselves on whatever money they were given by community members.

The secular clergy were men like the Parson in the *Tales*; they were local priests and church officials who did not belong to any particular order.

In addition to these legitimate church employees, a number of other, less savory characters attached themselves to the Church to make money. Among these were *pardoners*—men who would dispense "pardon" from sin for a fee. The Summoner in the *Tales* is a man who calls people to ecclesiastical (church) court; we see that, for the right price, he will let the summons drop.

Finally, women had positions in the Church that mirrored those of some of the men; nuns, for instance, were the female equivalent of monks. However, unlike the monks, the nuns were not considered ordained clergy. The Prioress is an example of a high-ranking nun. How much does she have in common with the Monk and the Friar?

Economy: During the fourteenth century, Europe was gradually moving from an economy based on *feudalism* to a more open, money-based system. Under feudalism, society had been organized into different levels of lord and servant; at the bottom were the serfs, who owned no property and had no rights as citizens, and at the very top was the supreme lord, the king. This system dated from a time when Europe was primarily agricultural, and had relied on the trading of needed services—a serf, for example, would supply farm labor to his lord in return for housing and protection. Society was now becoming more *urbanized*, though, and its new economy was based on money and goods. The Knight, Squire, Yeoman, and Franklin, as well as the Reeve, are remnants of the old feudal system, while the Merchant, Five Guildsmen, and even the Wife of Bath reflect the emergence of the new system.

Of course, the transformation in Europe's economy was not as simple as an overnight conversion from feudalism to a money system, but knowing that some of these changes were taking place, you can look for them in the *Canterbury Tales*.

Voice: Part of what makes the *Canterbury Tales* so complex is its multilayered structure. The narrator—who is not the same as Chaucer, the author—is retelling each pilgrim's story in that pilgrim's voice. Try to figure out who is really speaking: the author, the narrator, or the character. Is there ever a time when the character seems sincere, but the narrator or Chaucer is being ironic?

Language: You may be surprised at some of the words and images that Chaucer considered acceptable for literature. In fact, he himself, in the prologue to the Miller's Tale, apologizes for the obscenity he is "forced" to repeat. Why do you think he includes these kinds of stories?

Common Types of Story: Chaucer did not invent any of the stories he tells; he took the basic form of each from other sources. The Knight's Tale, for instance, is a typical story of *courtly love*—a romance in which a knight or gentleman goes to great lengths for a beautiful, seemingly unreachable woman. Tales that deliver a religious message or moral are based upon well-known fables and legends. What Chaucer does so creatively is to make these common stories say something about their teller. While we are reading about what happens in each tale, we are also sitting with the other pilgrims, watching the teller of the story and wondering about his or her own life.

The *General*
PROLOGUE

WHEN APRIL with his showers sweet with fruit
The drought of March has pierced unto the root
And bathed each vein with liquor that has power
To generate therein and sire the flower;
5 When Zephyr[1] also has, with his sweet breath,
Quickened again, in every holt[2] and heath,
The tender shoots and buds, and the young sun
Into the Ram[3] one half his course has run,
And many little birds make melody
10 That sleep through all the night with open eye
(So Nature pricks them on to ramp and rage)—
Then do folk long to go on pilgrimage,[4]
And palmers[5] to go seeking out strange strands,[6]
To distant shrines well known in sundry[7] lands.
15 And specially from every shire's[8] end
Of England they to Canterbury wend,[9]
The holy blessed martyr[10] there to seek
Who helped them when they lay so ill and weak.
    Befell that, in that season, on a day
20 In Southwark,[11] at the Tabard,[12] as I lay
Ready to start upon my pilgrimage
To Canterbury, full of devout courage,
There came at nightfall to that hostelry

[1] *the west wind*

[2] *wood*

[3] *the constellation Aries*

[4] *a journey to a sacred place; see glossary*

[5] *pilgrims*

[6] *shores*

[7] *various*

[8] *countryside's*

[9] *go*

[10] *Thomas a Becket, who was martyred at Canterbury; see glossary*

[11] *an area south of London bridge; in Chaucer's time, it had many inns and taverns*

[12] *the inn where the pilgrims are staying*

Some nine and twenty in a company
25 Of sundry persons who had chanced to fall
In fellowship, and pilgrims were they all
That toward Canterbury town would ride.
The rooms and stables spacious were and wide,
And well we there were eased, and of the best.
30 And briefly, when the sun had gone to rest,
So had I spoken with them, every one,
That I was of their fellowship anon,
And made agreement that we'd early rise

[13]*recount*

To take our way, as to you I'll devise.[13]
35 But nonetheless, whilst I have time and space,
Before yet farther in this tale I pace,
It seems to me accordant with reason
To inform you of the state of every one
Of all of these, as it appeared to me,
40 And who they were, and what was their degree,

[14]*dress*

And also what array[14] they all were in;
And with a knight thus will I first begin.

THE KNIGHT

A knight there was, and he a worthy man,
Who, from the moment that he first began

[15]*the code of behavior for knights*

To ride about the world, loved chivalry,[15]
Truth, honour, freedom and all courtesy.
5 At Alexandria[16], he, when it was won;

[16]*site of a Crusade; see glossary*

Of mortal battles he had fought fifteen,
And he'd fought for our faith at Tramissene[17]

[17]*city in modern-day Algeria*

And always won he sovereign fame for prize.
Though so illustrious, he was very wise
10 And bore himself as meekly as a maid.
He never yet had any vileness said,

[18]*man*

In all his life, to whatsoever wight.[18]
He was a truly perfect, gentle knight.
But now, to tell you all of his array,

[19]*coarse cloth*

15 His steeds were good, but yet he was not gay.
Of simple fustian[19] wore he a jupon[20]

[20]*sleeveless jacket*

Sadly discoloured by his habergeon;[21]

[21]*chain mail vest*

For he had lately come from his voyage
And now was going on this pilgrimage.

THE SQUIRE[22]

[22]*gentleman ranked below a knight*

With him there was his son, a youthful squire,
A lover and a lusty bachelor,
With locks well curled, as if they'd laid in press.
Some twenty years of age he was, I guess.
5 In stature he was of an average length,
Wondrously active, aye, and great of strength.
He'd ridden sometime with the cavalry
In Flanders, in Artois, and Picardy,[23]
And borne him well within that little space

[23]*sites in France and the Netherlands where English knights fought*

10 In hope to win thereby his lady's grace.
Embroidered was he, like a meadow bed
All full of freshest flowers, white and red.
Singing he was, or fluting, all the day;
He was as fresh as is the month of May.
15 Short was his gown, with sleeves both long and wide.[24]

[24]*the fashion of the day*

Well could he sit on horse, and fairly ride.
He could make songs and words thereto indite,
Joust, and dance too, as well as sketch and write.[25]
So hot he loved that, while night told her tale,

[25]*literacy was not widespread at this time, so this is a mark of the squire's class*

20 He slept no more than does a nightingale.
Courteous he, and humble, willing and able,
And carved before his father at the table.

THE YEOMAN[26]

[26]*a high-ranking servant*

A yeoman had he, nor more servants, no,
At that time, for he chose to travel so;
And he was clad in coat and hood of green.
A sheaf of peacock arrows bright and keen
5 Under his belt he bore right carefully
(Well could he keep his tackle yeomanly:
His arrows had no draggled feathers low),
And in his hand he bore a mighty bow.
A cropped head had he and a sun-browned face.
10 Of woodcraft knew he all the useful ways.
Upon his arm he bore a bracer[27] gay,
And at one side a sword and buckler,[28] yea,

[27]*arm guard*

[28]*shield*

And at the other side a dagger bright,
Well sheathed and sharp as spear point in the light;
15　On breast a Christopher of silver sheen.[29]
He bore a horn in baldric[30] all of green;
A forester he truly was, I guess.

THE PRIORESS[31]

There was also a nun, a prioress,
Who, in her smiling, modest was and coy;
Her greatest oath was but "By Saint Eloy!"[32]
And she was known as Madam Eglantine.[33]
5　Full well she sang the services divine
Intoning through her nose, becomingly;
And fair she spoke her French,[34] and fluently.
At table she had been well taught withal,
And never from her lips let morsels fall,
10　Nor dipped her fingers deep in sauce, but ate
With so much care the food upon her plate
That never driblet fell upon her breast.[35]
In courtesy she had delight and zest.
Her upper lip was always wiped so clean
15　That in her cup was no iota seen
Of grease, when she had drunk her draught of wine.
And certainly she was of great disport[36]
And full pleasant, and amiable of port[37]
And went to many pains to put on cheer
20　Of court, and very dignified appear,
And to be thought worthy of reverence.
But, to say something of her moral sense,
She was so charitable and piteous
That she would weep if she but saw a mouse
25　Caught in a trap, though it were dead or bled.
She had some little dogs, too, that she fed
On roasted flesh, or milk and fine white bread.[38]
But sore she'd weep if one of them were dead,
Or if men smote it with a rod to smart:
30　For pity ruled her, and her tender heart.
Full properly her wimple[39] pleated was.

[29]*Christopher was the patron saint of travelers*

[30]*sash*

[31]*supervisor of an abbey*

[32]*or St. Eligius; patron saint of goldsmiths*

[33]*her name means "honeysuckle"*

[34]*usually spoken by the upper classes*

[35]*notice the nun's dainty manners; where is her attention focused?*

[36]*well-bred ladies were supposed to be cheerful at social events*

[37]*behavior*

[38]*this kind of bread was very expensive*

[39]*nun's head covering*

Her nose was straight, her eyes as grey as glass,
Her mouth full small, and also soft and red;
But certainly she had a fair forehead;
35 It was almost a full span broad,[40] I own,
For, truth to tell, she was not undergrown.
Full stylish was her cloak, I was aware.
Of coral small about her arm she'd bear
A string of beads,[41] gauded[42] all round with green;
40 And from there hung a brooch of golden sheen
On which there was first written a crowned "A,"
And under, Amor Vincit Omnia.[43]

THE MONK[44]

A monk there was, one made for mastery,
An outrider,[45] who loved his venery;[46]
A manly man, to be an abbot able.
Full many a blooded horse had he in stable:
5 And when he rode men might his bridle hear
A-jingling in the whistling wind as clear,
Aye, and as loud as does the chapel bell
Where this brave monk was master of the cell.
The rule of Maurice[47] or Saint Benedict,[48]
10 By reason it was old and somewhat strict,
This said monk let such old things slowly pace
And followed new-world manners in their place.
He cared not for that text a clean-plucked hen
Which holds that hunters are not holy men
15 Nor that a monk, when he is cloisterless,
Is like unto a fish that's waterless;
That is to say, a monk out of his cloister.
But this same text he held not worth an oyster;
And I said his opinion was right good.
20 What? Should he study as a madman would
Upon a book in cloister cell? Or yet
Go labour with his hands and swink[49] and sweat,
As Austin[50] bids? How shall the world be served?
Let Austin have his swink to him reserved!
25 Therefore he was a rider day and night;

[40]*broad foreheads were highly fashionable*

[41]*rosary beads*

[42]*interspersed*

[43]*"Love Conquers All"*

[44]*clergymen who swore to withdraw from "worldly" affairs and live in a monastery; see glossary*

[45]*a monk who travels the countryside*

[46]*hunting*

[47]*disciple of St. Benedict*

[48]*founder of the Benedictine Rule, a guide to daily living for monks*

[49]*sweat*

[50]*St. Augustine, one of the Four Fathers of the Catholic Church*

Greyhounds he had, as swift as fowl in flight.
Since riding and the hunting of the hare
Were all his love, for no cost would he spare.
I saw his sleeves were lined around the hand
30 With fur of grey, the finest in the land;
Also, to fasten hood beneath his chin,
He had of good wrought gold a curious pin:
A love-knot in the larger end there was.
His head was bald and shone like any glass
35 And smooth as one anointed was his face.
Fat was this lord, he stood in goodly case.
His bulging eyes he rolled about, and hot
They gleamed, and red, like fire beneath a pot;
His boots were soft; his horse of great estate.
40 Now certainly he was a fine prelate:[51]
He was not pale as some poor wasted ghost.
A fat swan loved he best of any roast.
His palfrey[52] was as brown as is a berry.

THE FRIAR[53]

A friar there was, a wanton and a merry,
A limiter,[54] a very worthy man.
In all the Orders Four[55] is none that can
Equal his friendliness and fair language.
5 He had arranged full many a marriage
Of young women, and this at his own cost.
Unto his order he was a noble post.
Well liked by all and intimate was he
With franklins[56] everywhere in his country,
10 And with the worthy women of the town.
For very sweetly did he hear confession
And pleasant also was his absolution.[57]
He was an easy man to give penance[58]
When knowing he should gain a good pittance;[59]
15 For to a begging friar, money given
Is sign that any man has been well shriven.[60]
For if one gave (he dared to boast of this),
He took the man's repentance not amiss.

---

[51]*priest*

[52]*horse*

[53]*a clergyman who, unlike a monk, was supposed to tend to the affairs of the outside world; friars supported themselves by begging*

[54]*a friar licensed to beg in certain districts*

[55]*Augustinian, Dominican, Carmelite, Franciscan*

[56]*landowners*

[57]*implying that the friar exchanged forgiveness for sexual favors*

[58]*forgiveness*

[59]*small fee*

[60]*having made confession*

For many a man there is so hard of heart
He cannot weep however pains may smart.
20 Therefore, instead of weeping and of prayer,
Men ought to give some silver to the poor freres.
His tippet[61] was stuck always full of knives
And pins, to give to young and pleasing wives.
And certainly he kept a merry note:
25 Well could he sing and play upon the rote.[62]
At balladry he bore the prize away.
His throat was white as lily of the May;
Yet strong he was as any champion.
In towns he knew the taverns, every one,
30 And every host and gay barmaid also
Better than beggars and lepers did he know.
For unto no such solid man as he
Accorded it, as far as he could see,
To have sick lepers for acquaintances.
35 There is no honest advantageousness
In dealing with such poverty-stricken curs;
It's with the rich and with big victuallers.[63]
And so, wherever profit might arise,
Courteous he was and humble in men's eyes.
40 There was no other man so virtuous.
He was the finest beggar of his house;
A certain district being farmed to him,
None of his brethren dared approach its rim;
For though a widow had no shoes to show,
45 So pleasant was his *In principio*,[64]
He always got a farthing[65] ere he went.
He lived by pickings, it is evident.
And he could romp as well as any whelp.[66]
For he was not like a cloisterer,
50 With threadbare cope[67] as is the poor scholar,
But he was like a lord or like a pope.
Of double worsted[68] was his semi-cope,
That rounded like a bell, as you may guess.
He lisped a little, out of wantonness,
55 To make his English soft upon his tongue;
And in his harping, after he had sung,
His two eyes twinkled in his head as bright

[61]*hood*

[62]*fiddle*

[63]*food-sellers*

[64]*"In the beginning," the first words of the Old Testament*

[65]*coin*

[66]*puppy*

[67]*coat*

[68]*fine-knit*

As do the stars within the frosty night.
This worthy limiter was named Hubert.

THE MERCHANT[69]

There was a merchant with forked beard, and girt[70]
In motley[71] gown, and high on horse he sat,
Upon his head a Flemish beaver hat;
His boots were fastened rather elegantly.
5 His spoke his notions out right pompously,
Stressing the times when he had won, not lost.
He would the sea were held at any cost
Across from Middleburgh to Orwell town.
At money-changing he could make a crown.[72]
10 This worthy man kept all his wits well set;
There was no one could say he was in debt,
So well he governed all his trade affairs
With bargains and with borrowings and with shares.
Indeed, he was a worthy man withal,
15 But, sooth[73] to say, his name I can't recall.

THE CLERK[74]

A clerk from Oxford was with us also,
Who'd turned to getting knowledge, long ago.
As meagre was his horse as is a rake,
Nor he himself too fat, I'll undertake,
5 But he looked hollow and went soberly.
Right threadbare was his overcoat, for he
Had got him yet no churchly benefice,[75]
Nor was so worldly as to gain office.
For he would rather have at his bed's head
10 Some twenty books, all bound in black and red,
Of Aristotle[76] and his philosophy
Than rich robes, fiddle, or gay psaltery.[77]
Yet, and for all he was philosopher,
He had but little gold within his coffer;[78]
15 But all that he might borrow from a friend

On books and learning he would swiftly spend,
And then he'd pray right busily for the souls
Of those who gave him wherewithal for schools.
Of study took he utmost care and heed.
20 Not one word spoke he more than was his need;
And that was said in fullest reverence
And short and quick and full of high good sense.
Pregnant of moral virtue was his speech;
And gladly would he learn and gladly teach.

THE FIVE GUILDSMEN[79]

A haberdasher[80] and a carpenter,
An arras[81] maker, dyer, and weaver
Were with us, clothed in similar livery,[82]
All of one sober, great fraternity.
5   Their gear was new and well adorned it was;
Their weapons were not cheaply trimmed with brass,
But all with silver; chastely made and well
Their girdles and their pouches too, I tell.
Each man of them appeared a proper burgess[83]
10 To sit in guildhall on a high dais.[84]
And each of them, for wisdom he could span,
Was fitted to have been an alderman;[85]
For chattels they'd enough, and, too, of rent;
To which their good wives gave a free assent,
15 Or else for certain they had been to blame.
It's good to hear "Madam" before one's name,
And go to church when all the world may see,
Having one's mantle borne right royally.

THE COOK

A cook they had with them, just for the nones,[86]
To boil the chickens with the marrow-bones,
And flavour tartly and with galingale.[87]
Well could he tell a draught of London ale.
5   And he could roast and seethe and broil and fry,

[79] *craftsmen organized themselves into guilds; see* glossary

[80] *hat-maker*

[81] *curtain*

[82] *uniform*

[83] *citizen of a town*

[84] *platform*

[85] *local official*

[86] *occasion*

[87] *spice*

And make a good thick soup, and bake a pie.
But very ill it was, it seemed to me,
That on his shin a deadly sore[88] had he;
For sweet blanc-mange,[89] he made it with the best.

88 [perhaps from the plague]

89 white dessert resembling the sore

THE SAILOR

There was a sailor, living far out west;
For aught I know, he was of Dartmouth town.
He sadly rode a hackney,[90] in a gown,
Of thick rough cloth falling to the knee.
5 A dagger hanging on a cord had he
About his neck, and under arm, and down.
The summer's heat had burned his visage brown;
And certainly he was a good fellow.
Full many a draught of wine he'd drawn, I trow,[91]
10 Of Bordeaux vintage, while the trader slept.
Nice conscience was a thing he never kept.
If that he fought and got the upper hand,
By water he sent them home to every land.
But as for craft, to reckon well his tides,
15 His currents and the dangerous watersides,
His harbours, and his moon, his pilotage,
There was none such from Hull[92] to far Carthage.[93]
Hardy, and wise in all things undertaken,
By many a tempest had his beard been shaken.
20 He knew well all the havens, as they were,
From Gottland[94] to the Cape of Finisterre,[95]
And every creek in Brittany[96] and Spain;
His vessel had been christened Madeleine.

90 riding-horse

91 believe

92 port city in northeast England

93 city in Northern Africa

94 island off the coast of Sweden

95 in northwest Spain

96 region of north-west France

THE PHYSICIAN

With us there was a doctor of physic;
In all this world was none like him to pick
For talk of medicine and surgery;
For he was grounded in astronomy.[97]
5 He watched over his patients one and all
By hours[98] of his magic natural.[99]

97 some ailments and disorders were thought to result from the position of the stars and planets

98 astronomical measurements of time

99 astrology

He knew the cause of every malady,
Were it of hot or cold, of moist or dry,
And where engendered, and of what humour;[100]
10 He was a very good practitioner.
The cause being known, down to the deepest root,
Anon he gave to the sick man his boot.[101]
Ready he was, with his apothecaries,[102]
To send him drugs and all electuaries;[103]
15 By mutual aid much gold they'd always won—
Their friendship was a thing not new begun.
In diet he was measured as could be,
Including naught of superfluity,
But nourishing and easy to digest.
20 He rarely heeds what Scripture might suggest.
In blue and scarlet he went clad, withal,
Lined with a taffeta and with sendal;[104]
And yet he was right careful of expense;
He kept the gold he gained from pestilence.
25 For gold in physic is a fine cordial,[105]
And therefore loved he gold exceeding all.

THE WIFE OF BATH

There was a housewife come from Bath,[106] or near,
Who—sad to say—was deaf in either ear.
At making cloth she had so great a bent
She bettered those of Ypres and even of Ghent.[107]
5 Her kerchiefs were of finest weave and ground;
I dare swear that they weighed a full ten pound
Which, of a Sunday, she wore on her head.
Her hose were of the choicest scarlet red,
Close gartered, and her shoes were soft and new.
10 Bold was her face, and fair, and red of hue.
She'd been respectable throughout her life,
With five churched husbands bringing joy and strife,
Not counting other company in youth;
But thereof there's no need to speak, in truth.
15 Three times she'd journeyed to Jerusalem;[108]
And many a foreign stream she'd had to stem;

[100]*bodily fluid thought to govern mood*

[101]*cure*

[102]*pharmacists*

[103]*medical mixtures*

[104]*expensive silk*

[105]*tonic*

[106]*city in southwest England*

[107]*[Ypres and Ghent were towns in Flanders famous for their cloth]*

[108]*most important pilgrimage site because it was supposed to be the area in which Jesus preached, was crucified and buried*

At Rome[109] she'd been, and she'd been in Boulogne,[110]
In Spain at Santiago,[111] and at Cologne.[112]
She could tell much of wandering by the way:
20　Gap-toothed was she, it is no lie to say.
Upon an ambler easily she sat,
Well wimpled, aye, and over all a hat
As broad as is a buckler or a targe,[113]
A rug was tucked around her buttocks large,
25　And on her feet a pair of spurs quite sharp.
In company well could she laugh and carp.[114]
The remedies of love she knew, perchance,
For of that art she'd learned the old, old dance.

THE PARSON[115]

There was a good man of religion, too,
A country parson, poor, I warrant you;
But rich he was in holy thought and work.
He was a learned man also, a clerk,
5　Who Christ's own gospel truly sought to preach;
Devoutly his parishioners would he teach.
Benign he was and wondrous diligent.
Patient in adverse times and well content,
As he was oft times proven; always blithe,
10　He was right loath to curse to get a tithe,[116]
But rather would he give, in case of doubt,
Unto those poor parishioners about,
Part of his income, even of his goods.
Enough with little, coloured all his moods.
15　Wide was his parish, houses far asunder,
But never did he fail, for rain or thunder,
In sickness, or in sin, or any state,
To visit to the farthest, small and great,
Going afoot, and in his hand a stave.[117]
20　This fine example to his flock he gave,
That first he wrought and afterwards he taught;
Out of the gospel then that text he caught,
And this figure he added thereunto—
That, if gold rust, what shall poor iron do?

[109]*seat of the Pope*

[110]*pilgrimage site in France*

[111]*site of the shrine to Saint James de Compostela*

[112]*city in Germany that was also an important destination for religious pilgrims*

[113]*shield*

[114]*talk*

[115]*a local priest, whose job was to tend to the spiritual needs of the people in his parish and the surrounding countryside.*

[116]*the portion of a person's income that was supposed to be set aside for the Church*

[117]*shepherd's staff*

25 For if the priest be foul, in whom we trust,
  What wonder if a layman yield to lust?
  And shame it is, if priest take thought for keep,
  A shitty shepherd, shepherding clean sheep.
  Well ought a priest example good to give,
30 By his own cleanness, how his flock should live.
  He never let his benefice[118] for hire,
  Leaving his flock to flounder in the mire,
  And ran to London, up to old Saint Paul's[119]
  To get himself a chantry[120] there for souls,
35 But dwelt at home and kept so well the fold
  That never wolf could make his plans miscarry;
  He was a shepherd and not mercenary.
  And holy though he was, and virtuous,
  To sinners he was not impetuous,
40 Nor haughty in his speech, nor too divine,
  But in all teaching prudent and benign.
  To lead folk into Heaven but by stress
  Of good example was his busyness.
  But if some sinful one proved obstinate,
45 Be who it might, of high or low estate,
  Him he reproved, and sharply, as I know.
  There is nowhere a better priest, I trow.[121]
  He had no thirst for pomp or reverence,
  Nor made himself a special, spiced conscience,
50 But Christ's own lore, and His apostles' twelve
  He taught, but first he followed it himself.

THE PLOWMAN[122]

  With him there was a plowman, was his brother
  That many a load of dung, and many another
  Had scattered, for a good true toiler, he,
  Living in peace and perfect charity.
5 He loved God most, and that with his whole heart
  At all times, though he played or plied his art
  And next, his neighbour, even as himself.
  He'd thresh and dig, with never thought of pelf,[123]
  For Christ's own sake, for every poor wight

[118]*paid church office*

[119]*principal cathedral of London*

[120]*office in which a priest was paid to pray for people; usually a source of easy money*

[121]*believe*

[122]*supposed to represent a typical commoner, or member of the "third estate"; see glossary*

[123]*wealth*

10   All without pay, if it lay in his might.
     He paid his taxes, fully, fairly, well,
     Both by his own toil and by stuff he'd sell.
     In a tabard[124] he rode upon a mare.

THE MILLER[125]

     The miller was a stout churl,[126] be it known,
     Hardy and big of brawn and big of bone;
     Which was well proved, for when he went on lam
     At wrestling, never failed he of the ram.
 5   He was a chunky fellow, broad of build;
     He'd heave a door from hinges if he willed,
     Or break it through, by running, with his head.
     His beard, as any sow or fox, was red,
     And broad it was as if it were a spade.
10   Upon the coping[127] of his nose he had
     A wart, and thereon stood a tuft of hairs,
     Red as the bristles in an old sow's ears;
     His nostrils they were black and very wide.
     A sword and buckler bore he by his side.
15   His mouth was like a furnace door for size.
     He was a jester and could poetize,
     But mostly all of sin and ribaldries.[128]
     He could steal corn and full thrice charge his fees;
     And yet he had a thumb of gold,[129] begad.
20   A white coat and blue hood he wore, this lad.
     A bagpipe he could blow well, be it known,
     And with that same he brought us out of town.

THE MANCIPLE[130]

     There was a manciple from an inn of court,
     To whom all buyers might quite well resort
     To learn the art of buying food and drink;
     For whether he paid cash or not, I think
 5   That he so knew the markets, when to buy,
     He never found himself left high and dry.

[124]*loose shirt*

[125]*medieval stories sometimes presented millers as dishonest; Chaucer follows suit*

[126]*rude, coarse man*

[127]*top part*

[128]*obscene stories*

[129]*[Millers were said to cheat customers by putting their thumbs on the scale when they weighed grain]*

[130]*someone who purchased supplies for a school or monastery*

Now is it not of God a full fair grace
That such a vulgar man has wit to pace
The wisdom of a crowd of learned men?
10   Of masters had he more than three times ten,
Who were in law expert and curious;
Whereof there were a dozen in that house
Fit to be stewards of both rent and land
Of any lord in England who would stand
15   Upon his own and live in manner good,
In honour, debtless (save his head were wood),
Or live as frugally as he might desire;
These men were able to have helped a shire
In any case that ever might befall;
20   And yet this manciple outguessed them all.

THE REEVE[131]

The reeve he was a slender, choleric[132] man,
Who shaved his beard as close as razor can.
His hair was cut round even with his ears;
His top was tonsured[133] like a pulpiteer's.
5   Long were his legs, and they were very lean,
And like a staff, with no calf to be seen.
Well could he manage granary and bin,
No auditor could ever on him win.
He could foretell, by drought and by the rain,
10   The yielding of his seed and of his grain.
His lord's sheep and his oxen and his dairy,
His swine and horses, all his stores, his poultry,
Were wholly in this steward's managing;
And, by agreement, he'd made reckoning
15   Since his young lord of age was twenty years;
Yet no man ever found him in arrears.[134]
There was no agent, hind,[135] or herd[136] who'd cheat
But he knew well his cunning and deceit;
They were afraid of him as of the death.
20   His cottage was a good one, on a heath;
By green trees shaded with this dwelling-place.
Much better than his lord could he purchase.

[131]*an official in charge of overseeing a large estate*

[132]*irritable*

[133]*shaved on top, like a monk's*

[134]*owing money*

[135]*country laborer*

[136]*shepherd*

Right rich he was in his own private right,
Seeing he'd pleased his lord, by day or night,
25 By giving him, or lending, of his goods,
And so got thanked—but yet got coats and hoods.
In youth he'd learned a good trade, and had been
A carpenter, as fine as could be seen.
This steward sat a horse that well could trot,
30 And was all dapple-grey, and was named Scot.
A long surcoat[137] of blue did he parade,
And at his side he bore a rusty blade.
Of Norfolk[138] was this reeve of whom I tell,
From near a town that men call Badeswell.
35 Bundled he was like friar from chin to croup,[139]
And ever he rode hindmost of our troop.

THE SUMMONER[140]

A summoner was with us in that place,
Who had a fiery-red, cherubic face,
For eczema he had; his eyes were narrow.
As hot he was, and lecherous, as a sparrow;[141]
5 With black and scabby brows and scanty beard,
He had a face that little children feared.
There was no mercury, sulphur, or litharge,
No borax, ceruse, tartar[142] could discharge,
Nor ointment that could cleanse enough, or bite,
10 To free him of his boils and pimples white,
Nor of the bosses resting on his cheeks.
Well loved he garlic, onions, aye and leeks,
And drinking of strong wine as red as blood.
Then would he talk and shout as madman would.
15 And when a deal of wine he'd poured within,
Then would he utter no word save Latin.[143]
Some phrases had he learned, say two or three,
Which he had garnered out of some decree;
No wonder, for he'd heard it all the day;
20 And all you know right well that even a jay
Can call out "Wat" as well as can the pope.
But when, for aught else, into him you'd grope,

---

[137]outer coat

[138]an area in the East of England

[139]the rear of his horse

[140]a man who summoned people to Church court

[141][thought to be a highly sexual bird]

[142][substances thought to cleanse the skin]

[143]the language of the Church; the Summoner knows only a few phrases

'Twas found he'd spent his whole philosophy;
Just "Questio quid juris"[144] would he cry.
25 He was a noble rascal, and a kind;
A better comrade 'twould be hard to find.
Why, he would suffer, for a quart of wine,
Some good fellow to have his concubine
A twelve-month, and excuse him to the full
30 (Between ourselves, though, he could pluck a gull[145]).

THE PARDONER[146]

With him there rode a gentle pardoner
Straight from the court of Rome had journeyed he.
Loudly he sang "Come hither, love, to me,"
The summoner joining with a burden[147] round;
5 Was never horn of half so great a sound.
This pardoner had hair as yellow as wax,
But lank it hung as does a strike of flax;
In wisps hung down such locks as he'd on head,
And with them he his shoulders overspread;
10 But thin they dropped, and stringy, one by one.
But as to hood, for sport of it, he'd none,
Though it was packed in wallet all the while.
It seemed to him he went in latest style,
Dishevelled, save for cap, his head all bare.
15 His wallet lay before him in his lap,
Stuffed full of pardons brought from Rome all hot.
A voice he had that bleated like a goat.
No beard had he, nor ever should he have,
For smooth his face as he'd just had a shave;
20 I think he was a gelding[148] or a mare.
But in his craft, from Berwick unto Ware,[149]
Was no such pardoner in any place.
For in his bag he had a pillowcase
The which, he said, was Our True Lady's veil:
25 He said he had a piece of the very sail
That good Saint Peter[150] had, what time he went
Upon the sea, till Jesus changed his bent.
He had a latten[151] cross set full of stones,

[144] *a phrase used in church court*

[145] *pull a trick; also, engage in sexual intercourse*

[116] *a man who sells papal pardons for sin*

[147] *bass accompaniment*

[148] *castrated horse*

[149] *i.e., from one side of England to another*

[150] *an apostle whom Jesus ordered to walk upon the water*

[151] *brass*

And in a bottle had he some pig's bones.
30 But with these relics, when he came upon
Some simple parson, then this paragon
In that one day more money stood to gain
Than the poor dupe in two months could attain.
And thus, with flattery and suchlike japes,
35 He made the parson and the rest his apes.
But yet, to tell the whole truth at the last,
He was, in church, a fine ecclesiast.
Well could he read a lesson or a story,
But best of all he sang an offertory;
40 For well he knew that when that song was sung,
Then might he preach, and all with polished tongue,
To win some silver, as he right well could;
Therefore he sang so merrily and so loud.
Now have I told you briefly, in a clause,
45 The state, the array, the number, and the cause
Of the assembling of this company.

The Knight's
T A L E

ONCE ON A TIME, as old tales tell to us,
There was a duke whose name was Theseus;[1]
Of Athens he was lord and governor,
And in his time was such a conqueror
5 That greater was there not beneath the sun.
Full many a rich country had he won;
What with his wisdom and his chivalry
He gained the realm of Femininity,[2]
That was of old time known as Scythia.[3]
10 There wedded he the queen, Hippolyta,[4]
And brought her home with him to his country.
In glory great and with great pageantry,
And, too, her younger sister, Emily.
And thus, in victory and with melody,
15 Let I this noble duke to Athens ride.
With all his armed host marching at his side.
    This duke of whom I speak, of great renown,
When he had drawn almost unto the town,
In all well-being and in utmost pride,
20 He grew aware, casting his eyes aside,
That right upon the road, as suppliants do,
A company of ladies, two by two,

[1]legendary Greek king

[2]i.e., the realm of the Amazons, a legendary group of female warriors

[3]country in Asia Minor

[4]Queen of the Amazons

Knelt, all in black, before his cavalcade;
But such a clamorous cry of woe they made
25 That in the whole world living man had heard
No such a lamentation, on my word;
Nor would they cease lamenting till at last
They'd clutched his bridle reins and held them fast.
      "What folk are you that at my home-coming
30 Disturb my triumph with this dolorous thing?"
Cried Theseus. "Do you so much envy
My honour that you thus complain and cry?
Or who has wronged you now, or who offended?
Come, tell me whether it may be amended;
35 And tell me, why are you clothed thus in black?"
      The eldest lady of them answered back,
After she'd swooned, with cheek so deathly drear
That it was pitiful to see and hear,
And said: "Lord, to whom Fortune has but given
40 Victory, and to conquer where you've striven,
Your glory and your honour grieve not us;
But we beseech your aid and pity thus.
Have mercy on our woe and our distress.
Some drop of pity, of your gentleness,
45 Upon us wretched women, oh, let fall!
For see, lord, there is no one of us all
That has not been a duchess or a queen;
Now we are captives, as may well be seen:
Thanks be to Fortune and her treacherous wheel,

50 There's none can rest assured of constant weal.⁵
And truly, lord, expecting your return,
In Pity's temple, where the fires yet burn.
We have been waiting through a long fortnight;
Now help us, lord, since it is in your might."
55   "I, wretched woman, who am weeping thus,
Was once the wife of King Capaneus,
Who died at Thebes, oh, cursed be the day!
And all we that you see in this array,
And make this lamentation to be known,
60 All we have lost our husbands at that town
During the siege that round about it lay.
And now the old Creon, ah welaway!

The lord and governor of Thebes city,
Full of his wrath and all iniquity,
65 He, in despite and out of tyranny,
To do all shame and hurt to the bodies
Of our lord husbands, lying slain awhile,
Has drawn them all together in a pile,
And will not suffer them, nor give consent,
70 To buried be, or burned, nor will relent,
But sets his dogs to eat them, out of spite."
    And on that word, at once, without respite,
They all fell prone and cried out piteously.
"Have on us wretched women some mercy,
75 And let our sorrows sink into your heart!
    This gentle duke down from his horse did start
With heart of pity, when he'd heard them speak.
It seemed to him his heart must surely break,
And in his arms he took them tenderly,
80 Giving them comfort understandingly:
And swore his oath, that as he was true knight,
He would put forth so thoroughly his might
Against the tyrant Creon as to wreak
Vengeance so great that all of Greece should speak
85 And say how Creon was by Theseus served,
As one that had his death full well deserved.
This sworn and done, he no more there abode;
His banner he displayed and forth he rode
Toward Thebes, and all his host marched on beside.
90   Thus rode this duke, thus rode this conqueror,
And in his host of chivalry the flower,
Until he came to Thebes and did alight
Full in the field where he'd intent to fight.
But to be brief in telling of this thing,
95 With Creon, who was Thebes' dread lord and king,
He fought and slew him, manfully, like knight,
In open war, and put his host to flight;
And by assault he took the city then,
Levelling wall and rafter with his men;
100 And to the ladies he restored again
The bones of their poor husbands who were slain,
To do for them the last rites of that day.

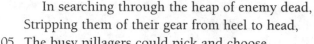

In searching through the heap of enemy dead,
Stripping them of their gear from heel to head,
105   The busy pillagers could pick and choose,
After the battle, what they best could use;
And so befell that in a heap they found,
Pierced through with many a grievous, bloody wound,
Two young knights lying together, side by side,
110   And of those two Arcita was the one,
The other knight was known as Palamon.
Not fully quick, nor fully dead they were,
But by their coats of arms and by their gear
The heralds readily could tell, withal,
115   That they were of the Theban blood royal,
And that they had been of two sisters born.
Out of the heap the spoilers had them torn
And carried gently over to the tent
Of Theseus; who shortly had them sent
120   To Athens, there in prison cell to lie
For ever, without ransom till they die.
And when this worthy duke had all this done,
He gathered host and home he rode anon,
With laurel crowned again as conqueror;
125   There lived he in all joy and all honour
His term of life; what more need words express?
And in a tower, in anguish and distress,
Palamon and Arcita, day and night,
Dwelt whence no gold might help them to take flight.
130   Thus passed by year by year and day by day,
Till it fell out, upon a morn in May,
That Emily, far fairer to be seen
Than is the lily on its stalk of green,
And fresher than is May with flowers new
135   (For with the rose's colour strove her hue,
I know not which was fairer of the two),
Before the dawn, as was her wont to do,
She rose and dressed her body for delight;
For May will have no sluggards of the night.
140   That season rouses every gentle heart
And forces it from winter's sleep to start,
Saying: "Arise and show thy reverence."

So Emily remembered to go thence
In honour of the May, and so she rose.
145 Clothed, she was sweeter than any flower that blows;
Her yellow hair was braided in one tress
Behind her back, a full yard long, I guess.
And in the garden, as the sun up-rose,
She sauntered back and forth and through each close,
150 Gathering many a flower, white and red,
To weave a delicate garland for her head;
And like a heavenly angel's was her song.
     The tower tall, which was so thick and strong,
And of the castle was the great donjon,
155 (Wherein the two knights languished in prison,
Of whom I told and shall yet tell, withal),
Was joined, at base, unto the garden wall
Whereunder Emily went dallying.
Bright was the sun and clear that morn in spring,
160 And Palamon, the woeful prisoner,
As was his wont, by leave of his jailer
Was up and pacing round that chamber high,
From which the noble city filled his eye,
And, too, the garden full of branches green,
165 Wherein bright Emily, fair and serene
Went walking and went roving up and down.
This sorrowing prisoner, this Palamon,
Being in the chamber, pacing to and fro,
And to himself complaining of his woe,
170 Cursing his birth, he often cried "Alas!"
And so it was, by chance or other pass,
That through a window, closed by many a bar
Of iron, strong and square as any spar,
He cast his eyes upon Emilia,
175 And thereupon he blenched and cried out "Ah!"
As if he had been smitten to the heart.
     And at that cry Arcita did up-start,
Asking: "My cousin, why what ails you now
That you've so deathly pallor on your brow?
180 Why did you cry out? Who's offended you?
For God's love, show some patience, as I do,
With prison, for it may not different be;

Fortune has given this adversity.
Some evil disposition or aspect

[6]*father of Jove and the other principal gods*

185 Of Saturn[6] did our horoscopes affect
To bring us here, though differently 'twere sworn;
But so the stars stood when we two were born;
We must endure it; that, in brief, is plain."
      This Palamon replied and said again:
190 "It's not our prison that caused me to cry.
But I was wounded lately through the eye
Down to my heart, and that my bane will be.
The beauty of the lady that I see
There in that garden, pacing to and fro,
195 Is cause of all my crying and my woe.
I know not if she's woman or goddess;
But Venus she is verily, I guess."
And thereupon down on his knees he fell,
And said: "O Venus,[7] if it be thy will

[7]*goddess of love*

200 To be transfigured in this garden, thus
Before me, sorrowing wretch, oh now help us
Out of this prison to be soon escaped.
And if it be my destiny is shaped,
By fate, to die in durance, in bondage,
205 Have pity, then upon our lineage
That has been brought so low by tyranny."
      And on that word Arcita looked to see
This lady who went roving to and fro.
And in that look her beauty struck him so
210 That, if poor Palamon is wounded sore,
Arcita is as deeply hurt, and more.
And with a sigh he said then, piteously:
"The virgin beauty slays me suddenly
Of her that wanders yonder in that place;
215 And save I have her pity and her grace,
That I at least may see her day by day,
I am but dead; there is no more to say."
      This Palamon, when these words he had heard,
Pitilessly he watched him, and answered:
220 "Do you say this in earnest or in play?"
      "Nay," quoth Arcita, "earnest, now, I say!
God help me, I am in no mood for play!

Palamon knit his brows and stood at bay.
"It will not prove," he said, "to your honour
225 After so long a time to turn traitor
To me, who am your cousin and your brother.
Sworn as we are, and each unto the other,
That never, though for death in any pain,
Never, indeed, till death shall part us twain,
230 Either of us in love shall hinder other,
No, nor in any thing, O my dear brother;
But that, instead you shall so further me
As I shall you. All this we did agree.
Such was your oath and such was mine also.
235 You dare not now deny it, well I know.
And now you would all falsely go about
To love my lady, whom I love and serve,
And shall while life my heart's blood may preserve.
Nay, false Arcita, it shall not be so.
240 I loved her first, and told you all my woe,
As to a brother and to one that swore
To further me, as I have said before.
For which you are in duty bound, as knight,
To help me, if the thing lie in your might,
245 Or else you're false, I say, and downfallen."
        Then this Arcita proudly spoke again:
"You shall," he said, "be rather false than I;
And that you're so, I tell you utterly;
For paramour[8] I loved her first, you know.
250 What can you say? You know not, even now,
Whether she is a woman or goddess!
Yours is a worship as of holiness,
While mine is love, as of a mortal maid;
Wherefore I told you of it, unafraid,
255 As to my cousin and my brother sworn.
Let us assume you loved her first, this morn;
Know you not well the ancient writer's saw
Of 'Who shall give a lover any law?'
Love is a greater law, aye by my pan,
260 Than man has ever given to earthly man.
And therefore statute law and such decrees
Are broken daily and in all degrees.

[8]*earthly love (i.e., object of sexual desire)*

A man must needs have love, maugre[9] his head.
He cannot flee it though he should be dead,
265 And be she maid, or widow, or a wife.
And yet it is not likely that, in life,
You'll stand within her graces; nor shall I;
For you are well aware, aye verily,
That you and I are doomed to prison drear
270 Perpetually; we gain no ransom here.
We strive but as those dogs did for the bone
They fought all day, and yet their gain was none.

10*scavenging bird*

Till came a kite[10] while they were still so wroth[11]
And bore the bone away between them both.

11*angry*

275 And therefore, at the king's court, O my brother,
It's each man for himself and not for other.
Love if you like; for I love and aye shall;
And certainly, dear brother, that is all.
Here in this prison cell must we remain
280 And each endure whatever fate ordain."
        Great was the strife, and long, betwixt the two,
If I had but the time to tell it you,
But to the point. It happened on a day
(To tell the tale as briefly as I may),
285 A worthy duke men called Pirithous,
Who had been friend unto Duke Theseus,
Since the time when they were very small
Was come to visit Athens and to call
His play-fellow, as he was wont to do,
290 For in this whole world he loved no man so;
And Theseus loved him as truly—nay,
So well each loved the other, old books say,
That when one died (it is but truth I tell),
The other went and sought him down in Hell,
295 But of that tale I have no wish to write.
Pirithous loved Arcita, too, that knight,
Having known him in Thebes full many a year;
And finally, at his request and prayer,
And that without a coin of ransom paid,
300 Duke Theseus released him out of shade,
Freely to go wherever he wished, and to
His own devices, as I'll now tell you.

The compact was, to set it plainly down,
That if Arcita, any time, were found,
305 Ever in life, by day or night, on ground
Of any country of this Theseus,
And he were caught, it was concerted thus,
That by the sword he straight should lose his head.
He had no choice, so taking leave he sped.
310 Let him beware, lest he should lose his head!
    How great is Arcita's sorrow now!
How through his heart he feels death's heavy blow;
He weeps, he wails, he cries out piteously;
To slay himself he now waits privately.
315 Said he: "Alas, the day that I was born!
I'm in worse prison, now, and more forlorn;
Now am I doomed eternally to dwell
No more in Purgatory,[12] but in Hell.
Alas, that I have known Pirithous!
320 For else had I remained with Theseus,
Fettered within that cell; but even so
Then had I been in bliss and not in woe.
Only the sight of her that I would serve,
Though I might never her dear grace deserve,
325 Would have sufficed, oh well enough for me!
O my dear cousin Palamon," said he,
"Yours is the victory, and that is sure,
For there, full happily, you may endure.
In prison? Never, but in Paradise!
330 Oh, well has Fortune turned for you the dice,
Who have the sight of her, I the absence.
For possible it is, in her presence,
You being a knight, a worthy and able,
That by some chance, since Fortune's changeable,
335 You may to your desire sometime attain.
But I, that am in exile and in pain,
Stripped of all hope and in so deep despair
That there's no earth nor water, fire nor air,
Nor any creature made of them there is
340 To help or give me comfort, now, in this—
Surely I'll die of sorrow and distress;
Farewell, my life, my love, my joyousness!"

[12]*according to Catholic theology, the area in which souls needing to be cleansed of sin must wait until they are ready to enter Heaven*

"Alas! Why is it men so much complain
Of what great God, or Fortune, may ordain,
345 When better is the gift, in any guise,
Than men may often for themselves devise?
One man desires only that great wealth
Which may but cause his death or long ill-health.
One who from prison gladly would be free,
350 At home by his own servants slain might be."
    And on the other hand, this Palamon,
When that he found Arcita truly gone,
Such lamentation made he, that the tower
Resounded of his crying, hour by hour.
355 The very fetters on his legs were yet
Again with all his bitter salt tears wet.
"Alas!" said he, "Arcita, cousin mine,
With all our strife, God knows, you've won the wine.
You're walking, now, in Theban streets, at large,
360 And all my woe you may from mind discharge.
You may, too, since you've wisdom and manhood,
Assemble all the people of our blood
And wage a war so sharp on this city
That by some fortune, or by some treaty,
365 You shall yet have that lady to your wife
For whom I now must needs lay down my life.
For surely 'tis in possibility,
Since you are now at large, from prison free,
And are a lord, great is your advantage
370 Above my own, who die here in a cage.
For I must weep and wail, the while I live,
In all the grief that prison cell may give,
And now with pain that love gives me, also,
Which doubles all my torment and my woe."
375   Now will I leave this Palamon, for he
Is in his prison, where he still must dwell,
And of Arcita will I forthwith tell.
Summer being passed away and nights grown long,
Increased now doubly all the anguish strong
380 Both of the lover and the prisoner.
I know not which one was the woefuller.
For, to be brief about it, Palamon

Is doomed to lie for ever in prison,
In chains and fetters till he shall be dead;
385 And exiled (on the forfeit of his head)
Arcita must remain abroad, nor see,
For evermore, the face of his lady.
    You lovers, now I ask you this question:
Who has the worse, Arcita or Palamon?
390 The one may see his lady day by day,
But yet in prison must he dwell for aye.
The other, where he wishes, he may go,
But never see his lady more, ah no.
Now answer as you wish, all you that can,
395 For I will speak right on as I began.
    Now when Arcita unto Thebes was come,
He lay and languished all day in his home,
Since he his lady nevermore should see,
But telling of his sorrow brief I'll be.
400 Had never any man so much torture,
No, nor shall have while this world may endure.
Bereft he was of sleep and meat and drink,
That lean he grew and dry as shaft, I think.
His eyes were hollow, awful to behold,
405 His face was sallow, pale and ashen-cold,
And solitary kept he and alone,
Wailing the whole night long, making his moan.
And so changed was he, that no man could know
Him by his words or voice, whoever heard.
410 And in this change, for all the world he fared
As if not troubled by malady of love,
But by that humor dark and grim, whereof
Springs melancholy madness in the brain,
And fantasy unbridled holds its reign.
415 And shortly, all was turned quite upside-down,
Both habits and the temper all had known
Of him, this woeful lover, Sir Arcita.
    Upon a night, while sleeping in his bed,
He dreamed of how the winged God Mercury,[13]
420 Before him stood and bade him happier be.
His sleep-bestowing wand he bore upright;
A hat he wore upon his ringlets bright.

[13]*the messenger god, who often appears in winged sandals and hat*

Arrayed this god was (noted at a leap)
As he'd been when to Argus[14] he gave sleep.

425 And thus he spoke: "To Athens shall you wend;
For all your woe is destined there to end."
And on that word Arcita woke and started.
"Now truly, howsoever sore I'm smarted,"
Said he, "to Athens right now will I fare;

430 Nor for the dread of death will I now spare
To see my lady, whom I love and serve;
I will not reck of death, with her, nor swerve."
    And with that word he caught a great mirror,
And saw how changed was all his old colour,

435 And saw his visage altered from its kind.
And right away it ran into his mind
That since his face was now disfigured so,
By suffering endured (as well we know),
He might, if he should bear him low in town,

440 Live there in Athens evermore, unknown,
Seeing his lady well-nigh every day.
And right anon he altered his array,
Like a poor labourer in low attire,
And all alone, save only for a squire,

445 Who knew his secret heart and all his case,
And who was dressed as poorly as he was,
To Athens was he gone the nearest way.
And to the court he went upon a day,
And offered service to do menial deeds

450 Fetch water, or whatever men should need.
And to be brief herein, and to be plain,
He found employment with a chamberlain[15]
Who was serving in the house of Emily;
For he was sharp and very soon could see

455 What every servant did who served her there.
Right well could he hew wood and water bear,
For he was young and mighty, let me own,
And big of muscle, aye and big of bone,
To do what any man asked in a trice.

460 A year or two he was in this service,
Page of the chamber of Emily the bright;
He said "Philostrates" would name him right.

But half so well beloved a man as he
Was never in that court, of his degree;
465 His gentle nature was so clearly shown,
That throughout all the court spread his renown.
They said it were but kindly courtesy
If Theseus should heighten his degree
And put him in more honourable service
470 Wherein he might his virtue exercise.
And thus, anon, his name was so up-sprung,
Both for his deeds and sayings of his tongue,
That Theseus had brought him nigh and nigher
And of the chamber he had made him squire,
475 And given him gold to maintain dignity.
Besides, men brought him, from his own country,
From year to year, clandestinely, his rent;
But honestly and slyly it was spent,
And no man wondered how he came by it.
480 And three years thus he lived, with much profit,
And bore him so in peace and so in war
There was no man that Theseus loved more.
And in such bliss I leave Arcita now,
And upon Palamon some words bestow.
485   In darksome, horrible, and strong prison
These seven years has now sat Palamon,
Wasted by woe and by his long distress.
Who has a two-fold heaviness
But Palamon? whom love yet tortures so
490 That half of his wits he is for woe;
And joined thereto he is a prisoner,
Perpetually, not only for a year.
And who could rhyme in English, properly,
His martyrdom? Forsooth, it is not I;
495 And therefore I pass lightly on my way.
     It fell out in the seventh year, in May,
On the third night (as say the books of old
Which have this story much more fully told),
Were it by chance or were it destiny
500 (Since, when a thing is destined, it must be),
That, shortly after midnight, Palamon,
By helping of a friend, broke from prison,

And fled the city, fast as he might go;
For he had given his guard a drink that so
505   Was mixed of spice and honey and certain wine
And opiates and sleeping powders fine,
That all that night, although a man might shake
This jailer, he slept on, nor could awake.
And thus he flees as fast as ever he may.
510   The night was short and it was nearly day,
Wherefore he needs must find a place to hide;
And to a grove that grew hard by, with stride
Of fearful foot then crept off Palamon.
In brief, he'd formed his plan, as he went on,
515   That in the grove he would lie fast all day,
And when night came, then would he take his way
Toward Thebes, and there find friends, and of them pray
Their help on Theseus in war's array;
And briefly either he would lose his life,
520   Or else win Emily to be his wife;
This is the gist of his intention plain.
          Now I'll return to Arcita again,
Who little knew how near to him was care
Till Fortune caught him in her tangling snare.
525   The busy lark, the herald of the day,
Salutes now in her song the morning grey;
And fiery Phoebus rises up so bright
That all the east is laughing with the light,
And with his streamers dries, among the greves,[16]
530   The silver droplets hanging on the leaves.
And so Arcita, in the court royal
With Theseus, and his squire principal,
Is risen, and looks on the merry day.
And now, to do his reverence to May,
535   Calling to mind the point of his desire,
He on a courser, leaping high like fire,
Is ridden to the fields to muse and play,
Out of the court, a mile or two away;
And to the grove, whereof I lately told,
540   By accident his way began to hold,
To make him there the garland that one weaves
Of woodbine leaves and of green hawthorn leaves.

[16]*leg-guards*

And loud he sang within the sunlit sheen:
"O May, with all thy flowers and all thy green,
545 Welcome be thou, thou fair and freshening May:
I hope to pluck some garland green today."
And on a path he wandered up and down,
Near which, and as it chanced, this Palamon
Lay in the thicket, where no man might see,
550 For sore afraid of finding death was he.
He knew not that Arcita was so near:
God knows he would have doubted eye and ear,
But it has been a truth these many years
That "Fields have eyes and every wood has ears."
555 It's well for one to bear himself with poise;
For every day unlooked-for chance annoys.
And little knew Arcita of his friend,
Who was so near and heard him to the end,
Where in the bush he sat now, keeping still.
560   Arcita, having roamed and roved his fill,
and having sung, began to speak,
And sat him down, sighing like one forlorn.
"Alas," said he, "the day that I was born!
How long, O Juno,[17] of thy cruelty,
565 Wilt thou wage bitter war on Thebes city?
Alas! Confounded beyond all reason
The blood of Cadmus and of Amphion;[18]
Of royal Cadmus, who was the first man
To build at Thebes, and first the town began,
570 And first of all the city to be king;
Of his lineage am I, and his offspring,
By true descent, and of the stock royal:
And now I'm such a wretched serving thrall,[19]
That he who is my mortal enemy,
575 I serve him as his squire, and all humbly.
And even more does Juno give me shame,
For I dare not acknowledge my own name;
But whereas I was Arcita by right,
Now I'm Philostrates, not worth a mite.
580 Alas, thou cruel Mars! Alas, Juno!
Thus have your angers all our kin brought low,
Save only me, and wretched Palamon,

[17]*Jove's wife and sister; also the goddess of marriage*

[18]*important figures in Thebes' history*

[19]*slave*

Whom Theseus martyrs yonder in prison.
And above all, to slay me utterly,
585 Love has his fiery dart so burningly
Struck through my faithful and care-laden heart,
My death was patterned ere[20] my swaddling-shirt.
You slay me with your two eyes, Emily;
You are the cause for which I now must die.
590 For on the whole of all my other care
I would not set the value of a tare,[21]
So I could do one thing to your pleasance!"
And with that word he fell down in a trance
That lasted long; and then he did up-start.
595   This Palamon, who thought that through his heart
He felt a cold and sudden sword blade glide,
For rage he shook, no longer would he hide.
But after he had heard Arcita's tale,
As he were mad, with face gone deathly pale,
600 He started up and sprang out of the thicket,
Crying: "Arcita, oh you traitor wicked,
Now are you caught, that crave my lady so,
For whom I suffer all this pain and woe,
And have befooled the great Duke Theseus,
605 And falsely changed your name and station thus:
Either I shall be dead or you shall die.
You shall not love my lady Emily,
But I will love her, and none other, no;
For I am Palamon, your mortal foe.
610 And though I have no weapon in this place,
Being but out of prison by God's grace,
I say again, that either you shall die
Or else forgo your love for Emily.
Choose which you will, for you shall not depart."
615   This Arcita, with scornful, angry heart,
When he knew him and all the tale had heard,
Fierce as a lion, out he pulled a sword
And answered thus: "By God that sits above!
Were it not you are sick and mad for love,
620 And that you have no weapon in this place,
Out of this grove you'd never move a pace,
But meet your death right now, and at my hand.

[20]*before*

[21]*small seed*

For I renounce the bond and its demand
Which you assert that I have made with you.
625 What, arrant fool, love's free to choose and do,
And I will have her, spite of all your might!
But in as much as you're a worthy knight
And willing to defend your love, in mail,
Hear now this word: tomorrow I'll not fail
630 (Without the cognizance[22] of any wight)
To come here armed and harnessed as a knight,
And to bring arms for you, too, as you'll see;
And choose the better and leave the worse for me.
And meat and drink this very night I'll bring,
635 Enough for you, and clothes for your bedding.
And if it be that you my lady win
And slay me in this wood that now I'm in,
Then may you have your lady, for all of me."
This Palamon replied: "I do agree."
640 And thus they parted till the morrow morn,
When each had pledged his honour to return.
Arcita rode into the town anon,
And on the morrow, ere the dawn, he bore,
Secretly, arms and armour out of store,
645 Enough for each, and proper to maintain
A battle in the field between the twain.[23]
And in the grove, at time and place they'd set,
Arcita and this Palamon were met.
There was no "good-day" given, no saluting,
650 But without word, rehearsal, or such thing,
Each of them helping, so they armed each other
As dutifully as he were his own brother;
And afterward, with their sharp spears and strong,
They thrust each at the other wondrous long.
655 You might have fancied that this Palamon,
In battle, was a furious, mad lion,
And that Arcita was a tiger quite:
Like very boars the two began to smite,
Like boars that froth for anger in the wood.
660 Up to the ankles fought they in their blood.
Clear was the day, as I have told ere this,
When Theseus, compact of joy and bliss,

[22]*recognition, awareness*

[23]*two*

With his Hippolyta, the lovely queen,
And fair Emilia, clothed all in green,
665 A-hunting they went riding royally.
And to the grove of trees that grew hard by,
In which there was a hart,[24] as men had told,
Duke Theseus the shortest way did hold.
And to the glade he rode on, straight and right,
670 For there the hart was wont to go in flight,
And over a brook, and so forth on his way.
This duke would have a course at him today,
With such hounds as it pleased him to command.
    And when this duke was come upon that land,
675 Under the slanting sun he looked, anon,
And there saw Arcita and Palamon
Who furiously fought, as two boars do;
The bright swords went in circles to and fro
So terribly, that even their least stroke
680 Seemed powerful enough to fell an oak;
But who the two were, nothing did he note.
This duke his courser with the sharp spurs smote
And in one bound he was between the two
And lugged his great sword out, and cried out: "Ho!
685 No more, I say, on pain of losing head!
By mighty Mars, that one shall soon be dead
Who smites another stroke that I may see!
But tell me now what manner of men ye be
That are so hardy as to fight out here
690 Without a judge or other officer,
As if you rode in lists[25] right royally?"
    This Palamon replied, then, hastily,
Saying: "O Sire, what need for more ado?
We have deserved our death at hands of you.
695 Two woeful wretches are we, two captives
That are encumbered by our own sad lives;
And as you are a righteous lord and judge
Give us not either mercy or refuge
But slay me first, for sacred charity,
700 But slay my fellow here, as well, with me.
Or slay him first; for though you've just learned it,
This is your foe, the prisoner Arcit

[24]deer

[25]jousting matches

That from the land was banished, on his head.
And for the which he merits to be dead.
705 For this is he who came unto your gate,
And said that he was known as Philostrate
Thus has he fooled you well this many a year,
And you have made him your chief squire, I hear:
And this is he that loves fair Emily.
710 For since the day is come when I must die,
I make confession plainly and say on,
That I am that same woeful Palamon
Who has your prison broken, viciously.
I am your mortal foe, and it is I
715 Who love so hotly Emily the bright
That I'll die gladly here within her sight.
  This worthy duke presently spoke again,
Saying: "This judgment needs but a short session:
Your own mouth, aye, and by your own confession,
720 Has doomed and damned you, as I shall record.
There is no need for torture, on my word.
But you shall die, by mighty Mars the red!"
But then the queen, whose heart for pity bled,
Began to weep, and so did Emily
725 And all the ladies in the company.
Great pity must it be, so thought they all,
That ever such misfortune should befall:
For these were gentlemen, of great estate,
And for no thing, save love, was their debate.
730 And all cried out—greater and less, they cried
"Have mercy, lord, upon us women all!"
And down upon their bare knees did they fall,
and would have kissed his feet there where he stood,
Till at the last assuaged was his high mood;
735 For soon will pity flow through gentle heart.
And though he first for ire did shake and start,
He soon considered, to state the case in brief,
What cause they had for fighting, what for grief;
And though his anger still their guilt accused,
740 Yet in his reason he held them both excused;
In such wise: he thought well that every man
Will help himself in love, if he but can,

And will himself deliver from prison;
And, too, at heart he had compassion on
745 Those women, for they cried and wept as one;
And in his gentle heart he thought anon,
And softly to himself he said then: "Fie
Upon a lord that will have no mercy,
But acts the lion, both in word and deed,
750 To those repentant and in fear and need,
As well as to the proud and pitiless man
That still would do the thing he began!
That lord must surely in discretion lack
Who, in such case, can no distinction make,
755 But weighs both proud and humble in one scale."
　　And shortly, when his ire was thus grown pale,
He looked up to the sky, with eyes alight,
And spoke these words, as he would promise plight:

[26]*goodness*

"The god of love, ah benedicite![26]
760 How mighty and how great a lord is he!
Against his might may stand no obstacles,
A true god is he by his miracles;
For he can manage, in his own sweet wise,
The heart of anyone as he devise.
765 Lo, here, Arcita and this Palamon,
That were delivered out of my prison,
And might have lived in Thebes right royally,
Knowing me for their mortal enemy,
And also that their lives lay in my hand;
770 And yet their love has willed them to this land,
Against all sense, and brought them here to die!
Look you now, is not that a folly high?
Who can be called a fool, except he love?
A man must play the fool, when young or old;
775 I know it of myself from years long gone:
For of love's servants I've been numbered one.
And therefore, since I know well all love's pain,
And know how sorely it can man constrain,
As one that has been taken in the net,
780 I will forgive your trespass, and forget,
At instance of my sweet queen, kneeling here,
Aye, and of Emily, my sister dear.

And you shall presently consent to swear
That nevermore will you my power dare,
785 Nor wage war on me, either night or day,
But will be friends to me in all you may;
I do forgive this trespass, full and fair."
    And then they swore what he demanded there,
And, of his might, they of his mercy prayed,
790 And he extended grace, and thus he said:
"To speak for royalty's inheritress,
Although she be a queen or a princess,
Each of you both is worthy, I confess,
When comes the time to wed: but nonetheless
795 I speak now of my sister Emily,
The cause of all this strife and jealousy—
You know yourselves she may not marry two
At once, although you fight or what you do:
One of you, then, and be he loath or lief,[27]
800 Must pipe his sorrows in an ivy leaf.
That is to say, she cannot have you both,
However jealous one may be, or wroth.
Therefore I put you both in this decree,
That each of you shall learn his destiny
805 As it is cast, and hear, now, in what wise
The word of fate shall speak through my device."
    "My will is this, to draw conclusion flat,
Without reply, or plea, or caveat[28]
(In any case, accept it for the best),
810 That each of you shall follow his own quest,
Free of all ransom or of fear from me;
And this day, fifty weeks hence, both shall be
Here once again, each with a hundred knights,
Armed for the lists, who stoutly for your rights
815 Will ready be to battle, to maintain
Your claim to love. I promise you, again,
Upon my word, and as I am a knight,
That whichsoever of you wins the fight,
That is to say, whichever of you two
820 May with his hundred, whom I spoke of, do
His foe to death, or out of boundary drive,
Then he shall have Emilia to wive

[27]*eager*

[28]*warning*

To whom Fortuna gives so fair a grace."
    I think that men would deem it negligence
825 If I forgot to tell of the expense
Of Theseus, who went so busily
To work upon the lists, right royally;
For such an amphitheatre he made,
Its equal never yet on earth was laid.
830   The day of their return is forthcoming,
When each of them a hundred knights must bring
The combat to support, as I have told;
And into Athens, covenant to uphold,
Has each one ridden with his hundred knights,
835 Well armed for war, at all points, in their mights.
And certainly, 'twas thought by many a man
That never, since the day this world began,
Speaking of good knights hardy of their hands,
Wherever God created seas and lands,
840 Was, of so few, so noble company.
For every man that loved all chivalry,
And eager was to win surpassing fame,
Had prayed to play a part in that great game;
And all was well with him who chosen was.
845   That Sunday night, ere day began to spring,
When Palamon the earliest lark heard sing,
Although it lacked two hours of being day
Yet the lark sang, and Palamon sang a lay.[29]
With pious heart and with a high courage
850 He rose, to go upon a pilgrimage
Unto the blessed Cytherea's shrine
(I mean Queen Venus,[30] worthy and benign).
And at her hour he then walked forth apace
Out to the lists wherein her temple was,
855 And down he knelt in manner to revere,
And from a full heart spoke as you shall hear.
    "Fairest of fair, O lady mine, Venus,
If thou wilt help, thus do I make my vow,
To boast of knightly skill I care not now,
860 Nor do I ask tomorrow's victory,
Nor any such renown, nor vain glory
Of prize of arms, blown before lord and churl,

[29]*poem set to music*

[30]*goodess of love*

But I would have possession of one girl,
Of Emily, and die in thy service;
865   Find thou the manner how, and in what wise.
For I care not, unless it better be,
Whether I vanquish them or they do me,
So I may have my lady in my arms.
For though Mars is the god of war's alarms,
870   Thy power is so great in Heaven above,
That, if it be thy will, I'll have my love.
Thy temple will I worship always so
That on thine altar, where'er I ride or go,
I will lay sacrifice and thy fires feed.
875   And if thou wilt not so, O lady, cede,
I pray thee, that tomorrow, with a spear,
Arcita bear me through the heart, just here.
For I'll care naught, when I have lost my life,
That Arcita may win her for his wife.
880   This the effect and end of all my prayer,
Give me my love, thou blissful lady fair."
      Now when he'd finished all the orison,[31]
His sacrifice he made, this Palamon,
Right piously, with all the circumstance,
885   Albeit I tell not now his observance.
But at the last the form of Venus shook
And gave a sign, and thereupon he took
This as acceptance of his prayer that day.
For though the signal came after delay
890   Yet he knew well that granted was his boon;[32]
And with glad heart he got him home right soon.
Three hours unequal[33] after Palamon
To Venus' temple at the lists had gone,
Up rose the sun and up rose Emily
895   And to Diana's temple did she hie.[34]
Her maidens led she thither, and with them
They carefully took fire and each emblem,
And incense, robes, and the remainder all
Of things for sacrifice ceremonial.
900   Her bright hair was unbound, but combed withal;
She wore of green oak leaves a coronal [35]
Upon her lovely head. Then she began

[31]*prayer*

[32]*prayer, request*

[33]*one of the hours between sunrise and sunset*

[34]*hurry*

[35]*crown*

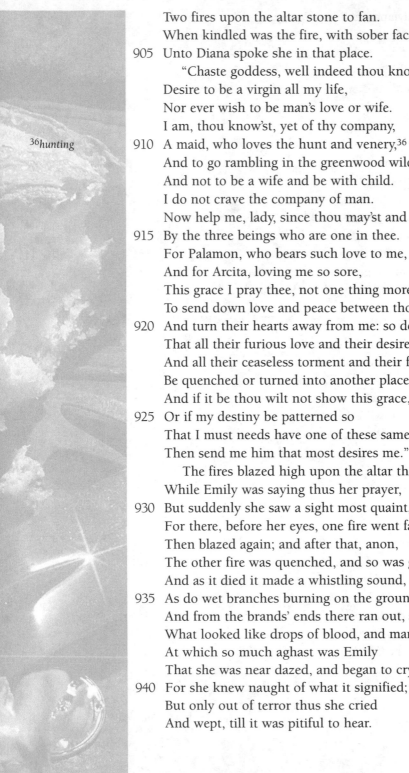

Two fires upon the altar stone to fan.
When kindled was the fire, with sober face
905 Unto Diana spoke she in that place.
    "Chaste goddess, well indeed thou knowest that I
Desire to be a virgin all my life,
Nor ever wish to be man's love or wife.
I am, thou know'st, yet of thy company,

36hunting

910 A maid, who loves the hunt and venery,[36]
And to go rambling in the greenwood wild,
And not to be a wife and be with child.
I do not crave the company of man.
Now help me, lady, since thou may'st and can,
915 By the three beings who are one in thee.
For Palamon, who bears such love to me,
And for Arcita, loving me so sore,
This grace I pray thee, not one thing more,
To send down love and peace between those two,
920 And turn their hearts away from me: so do
That all their furious love and their desire,
And all their ceaseless torment and their fire
Be quenched or turned into another place;
And if it be thou wilt not show this grace,
925 Or if my destiny be patterned so
That I must needs have one of these same two,
Then send me him that most desires me."
    The fires blazed high upon the altar there,
While Emily was saying thus her prayer,
930 But suddenly she saw a sight most quaint,
For there, before her eyes, one fire went faint,
Then blazed again; and after that, anon,
The other fire was quenched, and so was gone.
And as it died it made a whistling sound,
935 As do wet branches burning on the ground,
And from the brands' ends there ran out, anon,
What looked like drops of blood, and many a one;
At which so much aghast was Emily
That she was near dazed, and began to cry,
940 For she knew naught of what it signified;
But only out of terror thus she cried
And wept, till it was pitiful to hear.

But thereupon Diana did appear,
With bow in hand, like any right huntress,

945 And said "My daughter, leave this heaviness.
Among the high gods it has been affirmed,
And by eternal written word confirmed,
That you shall be the wife of one of those
Who bear for you so many cares and woes;

950 But unto which of them I may not tell.
Farewell, for I may not here longer dwell.
The fires which do upon my altar burn
Shall show to you, before you home return,
Your fortune with the lovers in this case.

955 And with that word, the arrows in the case
Of Diana did clatter loud and ring
And forth she went in mystic vanishing,
At which this Emily astonished was,
And said she then: "Ah, what means this, alas!

960 I put myself in thy protection here,
Diana, and at thy disposal dear."
And home she wended, then, the nearest way.
This is the purport; there's no more to say.
    At the next hour of Mars, and following this,

965 Arcita to the temple walked, that is
Devoted to fierce Mars, to sacrifice
With all the ceremonies, pagan-wise.[37]
With sobered heart and high devotion, on
This wise, right thus he said his orison.

970 "O mighty god that in the regions hold
In every realm and every land
The reins of battle in thy guiding hand,
And givest fortune as thou dost devise,
Accept of me my pious sacrifice.

975 If so it be that my youth may deserve,
And that my strength be worthy found to serve
Have pity, now, upon my pains that smart.
I'm young, and little skilled, as knowest thou,
With love more hurt, and much more broken now,

980 Than ever living creature was, I'm sure;
For she who makes me all this woe endure,
Cares not whether I sink or float in this

[37]*according to his pagan rituals*

And well I know, ere she mercy promise,
I must with courage win her in the place;
985 And well I know, without the help or grace
Of thee, none of my strength may me avail.
Then help me, lord, tomorrow not to fail:
As well as your hot fire now burneth me,
Ensure that I will then have victory.
990 Now, lord, have pity on my sorrows sore;
Give me the victory. I ask no more."
      With ended prayer of Arcita the strong,
The rings that on the temple door were hung,
And even the doors themselves, rattled so fast
995 That this Arcita found himself aghast.
The fires blazed high upon the altar bright,
Until the entire temple shone with light;
And a sweet odour rose up from the ground;
And Arcita whirled then his arm around,
1000 And yet more incense on the fire he cast,
And did still further rites; and at the last
The armour of God Mars began to ring,
And with that sound there came a murmuring,
Low and uncertain, saying: "Victory!"
1005 For which he gave Mars honour and glory.
And thus in joy and hope, which all might dare,
Arcita to his lodging then did fare,
Fain[38] of the fight as fowl is of the sun.
But thereupon such quarrelling was begun,
1010 From this same granting, in the heaven above,
Twixt lovely Venus, goddess of all love,
And Mars, the iron god armipotent,[39]
That Jove[40] toiled hard to make a settlement;
Until the sallow Saturn, calm and cold,
1015 Who had so many happenings known of old,
Found from his full experience the art
To satisfy each party and each part.
For true it is, age has great advantage;
Experience and wisdom come with age;
1020 Men may the old outrun, but not outwit.
Saturn anon, to make the fighters quit,
Although peacemaking goes against his kind,

[38]*desiring, eager*

[39]*powerfully armed*

[40]*king of the gods*

For all this strife begins to remedy find.
Now will I cease to speak of gods above,
1025 Of Mars and Venus, goddess of all love,
And tell you now, as plainly as I can,
The great result, for which I first began.
    A herald on a scaffold cried out "Ho!"
Till all the people's noise was stilled; and so
1030 When he observed that all were fallen still,
He then proclaimed the mighty ruler's will.
"The duke our lord, full wise and full discreet,
Holds that it were but wanton waste to meet
For gentle folk to fight all in the guise
1035 Of mortal battle in this enterprise.
Wherefore, in order that no man may die,
He does his earlier purpose modify.
No man, therefore, on pain of loss of life,
Shall any arrow, pole-axe, or short knife
1040 Send into lists in any wise, or bring;
Nor any shortened sword, for point-thrusting,
Shall a man draw, or bear it by his side.
Nor shall a knight against opponent ride,
Save one full course, with any sharp-ground spear;
1045 Unhorsed, a man may thrust with any gear.
And he that's overcome, should this occur,
Shall not be slain, but brought to barrier,
Whereof there shall be one on either side;
Let him be forced to go there and abide.
1050 And if by chance the leader there must go,
Of either side, or slay his equal foe,
No longer, then, shall tourneying endure.
God speed you; go forth now, and lay on sure.
With long sword and with maces fight your fill.
1055 Go now your ways; this is the lord duke's will."
    The voices of the people rent the skies,
Such was the uproar of their merry cries:
"Now God save such a lord, who is so good
He will not have destruction of men's blood!"
1060 Arcita and the hundred of his party
With banner red is entering anon;
And in that self-same moment, Palamon

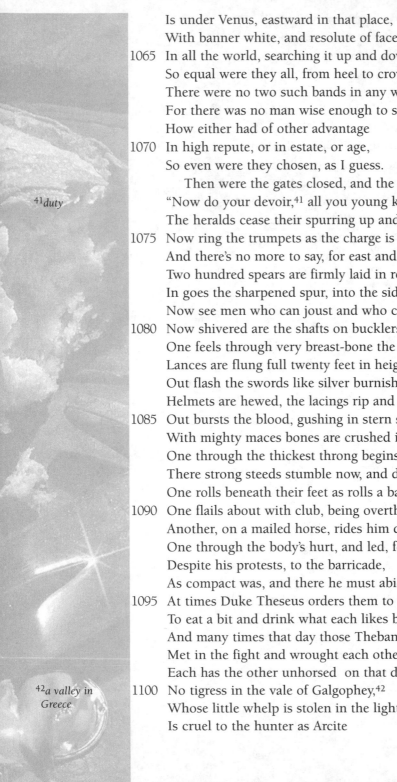

Is under Venus, eastward in that place,
With banner white, and resolute of face.
1065 In all the world, searching it up and down,
So equal were they all, from heel to crown,
There were no two such bands in any way.
For there was no man wise enough to say
How either had of other advantage
1070 In high repute, or in estate, or age,
So even were they chosen, as I guess.
 Then were the gates closed, and the cry rang loud:
"Now do your devoir,[41] all you young knights proud!"
The heralds cease their spurring up and down;
1075 Now ring the trumpets as the charge is blown;
And there's no more to say, for east and west
Two hundred spears are firmly laid in rest;
In goes the sharpened spur, into the side.
Now see men who can joust and who can ride!
1080 Now shivered are the shafts on bucklers thick;
One feels through very breast-bone the spear's prick;
Lances are flung full twenty feet in height;
Out flash the swords like silver burnished bright.
Helmets are hewed, the lacings rip and shred;
1085 Out bursts the blood, gushing in stern streams red.
With mighty maces bones are crushed in joust.
One through the thickest throng begins to thrust.
There strong steeds stumble now, and down goes all.
One rolls beneath their feet as rolls a ball.
1090 One flails about with club, being overthrown,
Another, on a mailed horse, rides him down.
One through the body's hurt, and led, for aid,
Despite his protests, to the barricade,
As compact was, and there he must abide.
1095 At times Duke Theseus orders them to rest,
To eat a bit and drink what each likes best.
And many times that day those Thebans two
Met in the fight and wrought each other woe;
Each has the other unhorsed on that day.
1100 No tigress in the vale of Galgophey,[42]
Whose little whelp is stolen in the light,
Is cruel to the hunter as Arcite

[41]*duty*

[42]*a valley in Greece*

For jealousy is cruel to Palamon;
Nor in Belmarie,[43] when the hunt is on

1105 Is there a lion, wild for want of food,
That of his prey desires so much the blood
As Palamon the death of Arcite there.
Their jealous blows fall on their helmets fair;
Out leaps the blood and makes their two sides red.

1110   But sometime comes the end of every deed;
And ere the sun had sunk to rest in gold,
The mighty King Emetreus did hold
This Palamon, as he fought with Arcita,
And made his sword deep in the flesh to bite;

1115 And by the force of twenty men he's made,
Unyielded, to withdraw to barricade.
And, trying hard to rescue Palamon,
The mighty King Lycurgus is borne down;
And King Emetreus, for all his strength,

1120 Is hurled out of the saddle a sword's length,
So hits out Palamon once more, or ere
(But all for naught) he's brought to barrier.
His hardy heart may now avail him naught;
He must abide there now, being fairly caught

1125 By force of arms, as by provision known.
    Who sorrows now but woeful Palamon,
Who may no more advance into the fight?
And when Duke Theseus had seen this sight,
Unto the warriors fighting, every one,

1130 He cried out: "Hold! No more! For it is done!
Now will I prove true judge, of no party.
Theban Arcita shall have Emily,
Who, by his fortune, has her fairly won."
    But now, what can fair Venus do above?

1135 What says she now? What does this queen of love
But weep so fast, for thwarting of her will,
Her tears upon the lists begin to spill.
She said: "Now am I shamed and over-flung."
But Saturn said: "My daughter, hold your tongue.

1140 Mars has his will, his knight has all his boon,
And, by my head, you shall be eased, and soon."
    The hearalds that did loudly yell and cry,

Were at their best for joy Sir Arcit.
But listen now—leave off your noise a bit—
1145 to the miracle that happened there anon.
This fierce Arcita doffs his helmet soon,
And mounted on a horse, to show his face,
He spurs from end to end of that great place,
Looking aloft to gaze on Emily;
1150 And she cast down on him a friendly eye
(For women, generally speaking, go
Wherever Fortune may her favor show);
And she was fair to see, and held his heart.
But from the ground infernal furies start,
1155 From Pluto sent, at instance of Saturn,
Whereat his horse, for fear, began to turn
And leap aside, all suddenly falling there;
And Arcita before he could beware
Was pitched upon the ground, upon his head
1160 And lay there, moving not, as he were dead,
So ran the surging blood into his face.
Anon they carried him from out that place,
With heavy hearts, to Theseus' palace.
There was his harness cut away, each lace,
1165 And swiftly was he laid upon a bed,
For he was yet alive and some words said,
Crying and calling after Emily.

Swells now Arcita's breast until the sore
Increases near his heart yet more and more.
1170 The clotted blood, in spite of all leech-craft,
Rots in his bulk, and there it must be left,
Since no device of skillful blood-letting,
Nor drink of herbs, can help him in this thing.
All is so broken in that part of him,
1175 Nature retains no vigour there, nor vim.
The sum of all is, Arcita must die,
And so he sends a word to Emily,
And Palamon, who was his cousin dear;
And then he said to them as you shall hear.
1180 "To you, my lady, whom I love the most;
But I bequeath the service of my ghost
To you above all others, this being sure

Now that my life may here no more endure.
Alas, the woe! Alas, the pain so strong
1185 That I for you have suffered, and so long!
Alas for death! Alas, my Emily!
Alas, the parting of our company!
Alas, my heart's own queen! Alas, my wife!
My soul's dear lady, ender of my life!
1190 Farewell, my sweet foe! O my Emily!
Oh, take me in your gentle arms, I pray,
For love of God, and hear what I will say."
  "I have here, with my cousin Palamon,
Had strife and rancour many a day that's gone,
1195 For love of you and for my jealousy.
May Jove so surely guide my soul for me,
To speak about a lover properly.
In this world, right now, I know of none
So worthy to be loved as Palamon,
1200 Who serves you and will do so all his life.
And if you ever should become a wife,
Forget not Palamon, the noble man."
  And with that word his speech to fail began,
For from his feet up to his breast had come
1205 The cold of death, making his body numb.
And furthermore, from his two arms the strength
Was gone out, now, and he was lost, at length.
Only the intellect, and nothing more,
Which dwelt within his heart so sick and sore,
1210 Began to fail now, when the heart felt death,
And his eyes darkened, and he failed of breath.
But on his lady turned he still his eye,
And his last word was, "Mercy, Emily!"
His spirit changed its house and went from here.
1215 As I was never there, I can't say where.
Now will I speak forthwith of Emily.
  Shrieked Emily and howled now Palamon,
Till Theseus his sister took, anon,
And bore her, swooning for the corpse, away.
1220 How shall it help, to dwell the livelong day
In telling how she wept both night and morrow?
For in like cases women have such sorrow,

When their good husband from their side must go,
And, for the greater part, they take on so,
1225 Or else they fall into such malady
That, at the last, and certainly, they die.
Infinite were the sorrows and the tears
Of all old folk and folk of tender years
Throughout the town, at death of this Theban;
1230 For him there wept the child and wept the man;
So great a weeping was not, 'tis certain,
When Hector was brought back, but newly slain,
To Troy. Alas, the sorrow that was there!
Tearing of cheeks and rending out of hair.
1235 "Oh why will you be dead," these women cry,
"Who had of gold enough, and Emily?"
No man might comfort then Duke Theseus,
Excepting his old father, Aegeus,
Who knew this world's mutations, and men's own,
1240 Since he had seen them changing up and down,
Joy after woe, and woe from happiness:
He showed them, by example, the process.
"Just as there never died a man," quoth he,
"But he had lived on earth in some degree,
1245 Just so there never lived a man," he said,
"In all this world, but must be sometime dead.
This world is but a thoroughfare of woe,
And we are pilgrims passing to and fro;
Death is the end of every worldly sore."
1250 And after this, he told them yet much more
To that effect, all wisely to exhort
The people that they should find some comfort.
Duke Theseus now considered and with care
What place of burial he should prepare
1255 For good Arcita, as it best might be,
And one most worthy of his high degree.
And at the last concluded, hereupon,
That where at first Arcita and Palamon
Had fought for love, with no man else between,
1260 There in that very grove, so sweet and green,
Where he mused on his amorous desires
Complaining of love's hot and flaming fires,

He'd make a pyre and have the funeral.
Accomplished there, and worthily in all.
1265 And so he gave command to hack and hew
The ancient oaks, and lay them straight and true
In split lengths that would kindle well and burn.
His officers, with sure swift feet, they turn
And ride away to do his whole intent.
1270 And after this Duke Theseus straightway sent
For a great bier, and had it all o'er-spread
With cloth of gold, the richest that he had.
Arcita clad he, too, in cloth of gold;
White glove were on his hands where they did fold;
1275 Upon his head a crown of laurel green,
And near his hand a sword both bright and keen.
Then, having bared the dead face on the bier,
The duke so wept,'twas pitiful to hear.
And, so that folk might see him, one and all,
1280 When it was day he brought them to the hall
Which echoed of their wailing cries anon.
Then came this woeful Theban, Palamon,
With fluttery beard and matted, ash-strewn hair,
All in black clothes wet with his tears; and there,
1285 Surpassing all in weeping, Emily,
The most affected of the company.
   The noblest Greeks did gladly volunteer
To bear upon their shoulders that great bier,
With measured pace and eyes gone red and wet,
1290 Through all the city, by the wide main street,
Which was all spread with black, and, wondrous high,
Covered with this same cloth were houses nigh.
Upon the right hand went old Aegeus,
And on the other side Duke Theseus,
1295 With vessels in their hands, of gold right fine,
All filled with honey, milk, and blood, and wine;
And Palamon with a great company;
And after that came woeful Emily,
With fire in hands, as use was, to ignite
1300 The sacrifice and set the pyre alight.
   Great labour and full great apparelling
Went to the service and the fire-making.

That is to say, the branches were so broad.
Of straw there first was laid full many a load.
1305 But how the fire was made to climb so high;
Or what names all the different trees went by,
Or how they were felled, shan't be told by me.

[44]pale

Nor how aghast[44] the ground was in the light,
Not being used to seeing the sun so bright;
1310 Nor how the fire was started first with straw,
And then dry sticks cut into thirds by a saw,

[45][fine oils and spices were thrown onto funeral fires]

And then with green wood and with spicery,[45]
And then with cloth of gold and jewelery
And garlands hanging with full many a flower,
1315 And myrrh, and incense, sweet as rose in bower;
Nor how Arcita lies among all this,
Nor what vast wealth about his body is;
Nor how this Emily, as was their way,
Lighted the sacred funeral fire, that day,
1320 Nor how she swooned when men built up the fire,
Nor what she said, nor what was her desire;
No, nor what gems men on the fire then cast,
When the white flame went high and burned so fast;
Nor how one cast his shield, and one his spear,

[46]clothes

1325 And some their vestments,[46] on that burning bier,
With cups of wine, and cups of milk, and blood,
Into that flame, which burned as wild-fire would;
Nor how the Greeks, in one huge wailing rout,
Rode slowly three times all the fire about,
1330 Upon the left hand, with a loud shouting,
And three times more, with weapons clattering,
While thrice the women there raised up a cry;
Nor how was homeward led sad Emily;
Nor how Arcita burned to ashes cold;

[47][the ancient Greeks observed major funerals by holding athletic games]

1335 All that same night, nor how the Greeks did play[47]
Who, naked, wrestled best, with oil anointed,
Nor who best bore himself in deeds appointed.
I will not even tell how they were gone
Home, into Athens, when the play was done;
1340 But briefly to the point, now, will I wend
And make of this, my lengthy tale, an end.
With passing in their length of certain years,

All put by was the mourning and the tears
Of Greeks, as by one general assent;

1345 And then it seems there was a parliament
At Athens, upon certain points in case;
Among the which points spoken of there was
The ratifying of alliances
That should hold Thebes from all defiances.

1350 Whereat this noble Theseus, anon,
Invited there the gentle Palamon,
Not telling him what was the cause and why;
But in his mourning clothes, and sorrowfully,
He came upon that bidding, so say I.

1355 And then Duke Theseus sent for Emily.
When they were seated and was hushed the place,
And Theseus had mused a little space,
Ere any word came from his full wise breast,
His two eyes fixed on whoso pleased him best,

1360 Then with a sad face sighed he deep and still,
And after that began to speak his will.
  "When first God forged the goodly chain of love,
Great the effect, and high was His intent;
Well knew He why, and what thereof He meant;

1365 For with that goodly chain of love He bound
The fire, the air, the water, and dry ground
In certain bounds, the which they might not flee;
That same First Cause and Mover,"[48] then quoth he,
"Has stablished in this base world, up and down,

1370 A certain length of days to call their own
For all that are engendered in this place,
Beyond the which not one day may they pace,
Though yet all may that certain time abridge;
Authority there needs none, I allege,

1375 For it is well proved by experience.
Well may man know, unless he be a fool
That every part derives but from the whole,
And therefore, of His Wisdom's Providence,
Has He so well established ordinance

1380 That species of all things and all progressions,
If they'd endure, it must be by successions,
Not being themselves eternal, 'tis no lie:

[48]*God*

This may you understand and see by eye."
    "Lo now, the oak, that has long nourishing
1385 Even from the time that it begins to spring,
And has so long a life, as we may see,
Yet at the last all wasted is the tree.
"Consider, too, how even the hard stone
Under our feet we tread each day upon
1390 Yet wastes it, as it lies beside the way.
And the broad river will be dry some day.
And great towns wane; we see them vanishing.
Thus may we see the end to everything."
    "Of man and woman just the same is true:
1395 Needs must, in either season of the two,
That is to say, in youth or else in age,
All men perish, the king as well as page;
Some in their bed, and some in the deep sea,
And some in the wide field—as it may be;
1400 There's naught will help; all go the same way. Aye,
Then may I say that everything must die.
Who causes this but Jupiter the King?
He is the Prince and Cause of everything,
Converting all back to that primal well
1405 From which it was derived, 'tis sooth to tell.
And against this, for every thing alive,
Of any state, avails it not to strive.
    "Then is it wisdom, as it seems to me,
To make a virtue of necessity,
1410 And calmly take what we may not eschew,
And specially that which to all is due.
Whoso would balk at aught, he does folly,
And thus rebels against His potency.
And certainly a man has most honour
1415 In dying in his excellence and flower,
When he is certain of his high good name;
For then he gives to friend, and self, no shame.
And gladder ought a friend be of his death
When, in much honour, he yields up his breath,
1420 Than when his name's grown feeble with old age;
For all forgotten, then, is his courage.
Hence it is best for all of noble name

To die when at the summit of their fame.
The contrary of this is wilfulness.
1425 Why do we grumble? Why have heaviness
That good Arcita, chivalry's fair flower,
Is gone, with honour, in his best-lived hour,
Out of the filthy prison of this life?
Why grumble here his cousin and his wife
1430 About his welfare, who loved them so well?
Can he thank them? Nay, God knows, not! Nor tell
How they his soul and their own selves offend."
 "What may I prove by this long argument
Save that we all turn to merriment,
1435 After our grief, and give Jove thanks for grace.
And so, before we go from out this place,
I counsel that we make, of sorrows two,
One perfect joy, lasting for aye, for you;
And look you now, where most woe is herein,
1440 There will we first amend it and begin.
 "Sister," quoth he, "you have my full consent,
With the advice of this my Parliament,
That gentle Palamon, your own true knight,
Who serves you well with will and heart and might,
1455 And so has ever, since you knew him first—
That you shall, of your grace, allay his thirst
By taking him for husband and for lord:
Lend me your hand, for this is our accord.
Let now your woman's pity make him glad.
1450 For he is a king's brother's son, by gad;
And though he were a poor knight bachelor,
Since he has served you for so many a year,
And borne for you so great adversity,
This ought to weigh with you, it seems to me,
1455 For mercy ought to dominate mere right."
 Then said he thus to Palamon the knight:
"I think there needs but little sermoning
To make you give consent, now, to this thing.
Come near, and take your lady by the hand."
1460 Between them, then, was tied that nuptial band,
Which is called matrimony or marriage,
By all the council and the baronage.

And thus, in all bliss and with melody,
Has Palamon now wedded Emily.
1465 And God, Who all this universe has wrought,
Send him His love, who has it dearly bought.
For now has Palamon, in all things, wealth,
Living in bliss, in riches, and in health;
And Emily loved him so tenderly,
1470 And he served her so well and faithfully,
That never word once marred their happiness,
No jealousy, nor other such distress.
Thus ends now Palamon and Emily;
And may God save all this fair company! Amen.

The Miller's
PROLOGUE

WHEN THAT THE Knight had thus his story told,
In all the crowd there was not young or old
Who didn't say it was a noble story
And worthy to be called into memory.
5 The high-born ones, especially, felt this way.
Our host did laugh and swear, "So I daresay,
This goes quite well; unbuckled is the sack.
Let 's see now who shall give a story back.
For certainly the game is well began.
10 Now tell to us, Sir Monk, if that you can
Something to measure up to the Knight's tale."
The Miller, drunk enough to be all pale,
So that barely upon his horse he sat,
He would not lower neither hood nor hat,
15 Nor wait for any out of courtesy,
But in the voice of Pilate[1] 'gan to cry,
And then he swore, "By arms, by bones and blood,
I know a noble story for this crowd,
With which I will now equal the Knight's tale."
20 Our Host saw that the monk was drunk on ale,
And said, "Hold off awhile, Robyn, dear brother;
Some better man shall first tell us another.

[1]*i.e., a loud voice, like the character of Pilate in medieval religious plays*

Hold off, and let us do this properly."
"By soul of God,"said he, "that will not I;
25 For I will speak, or else go on my way."
Our Host answered, "Tell on, by devil's way!
You are a fool; your wit is overcome."
"Now hearken," said the Miller, "all and some—
But first I make the protest all around
30 That I am drunk; I know it by my sound.
And therefore if I misspeak or missay,
Blame that on ale of Southwark, I you pray.
For I will tell a legend and a life
Both of a carpenter and of his wife,
35 How that a clerk hath set the woodwright's cap."
The Reeve answered and said, "Stop your claptrap!
Let be your lewd and drunken harlotry.
It is a sin and also great folly
To injure any man, or him defame,
40 And to bring wives into this kind of fame.
You have enough of other tales to spin."
This drunken miller spoke full soon again
And said, "My dearest brother Osewold,
A man who has no wife is no cuckold.
45 But I say not that therefore you are one;
There have been quite good women, many a one,
And ever a thousand good against one bad.
You know this well yourself, unless you're mad.
Why are you angry with my story now?
50 I have a wife, by God, as well as thou;
Yet won't I, for the oxen at my trough,
Take on more than I know to be enough
And say about myself that I am one;
I will believe truly that I am none.
55 A husband shall not be inquisitive
Of God's secrets, nor how his woman lives.
As long as he finds God's plenty in her,
Of all the rest he needs not to inquire."
What have I more to say, but this miller
60 Would not his words for any man defer,
But told his boorish tale in his own style.
I feel regret repeating it this while.

And therefore, every proper man, I pray,
For love of God, do not take what I say
65 As meant in evil, for I must rehearse
All of their tales, be they better or worse.
For if I don't, I'm false to my subject.
And therefore, anyone who might object ,
Now turn the page and choose another tale;
70 For he shall find enough, both great and small,
Of history that deals with nobleness,
And, too, morality and holiness.
And don't blame me if you should choose amiss.
The Miller is a churl,[2] you well know this.
75 So was the Reeve also and others too,
And harlotry was in their stories two.
Advise yourself, and put me out of blame,
For men should not make earnest of a game.

[2]*rude, coarse man*

The Miller's
T A L E

ONCE ON A TIME was dwelling in Oxford
A wealthy lout[1] who took in guests to board,
And of his craft he was a carpenter.
A poor scholar was lodging with him there,
5 Who'd learned the arts, but all his fantasy[2]
Was turned to study of astrology;
And knew a certain set of theorems
And could find out by various strategems,
If men but asked of him in certain hours
10 When they should have a drought or else have showers,
Or if men asked of him what should befall
To anything—I cannot list them all.
    This clerk was called the clever Nicholas;
Of secret loves he knew and their solace;
15 And he kept counsel, too, for he was sly
And meek as any maiden passing by.
He had a chamber in that hostelry,
And lived alone there, with no company,
All garnished with sweet herbs of good repute;
20 And he himself sweet-smelling as the root
Of licorice, valerian, or setwall.[3]
His *Almagest,*[4] and books both great and small

[1]*brute*

[2]*hobby*

[3]*sweet herbs*

[4]*book on astrology*

71

5an instrument
 used to calculate
 the positions of
 stars and planets

6counting stones

7harp

8medieval carol

9a popular tune

10man cheated on
 by his wife

11Roman writer
 often cited by
 medieval authors

12flare

13headband

14lecherous

15fruit related to a
 plum

His astrolabe,[5] belonging to his art,
His algorism stones[6]—all laid apart
25 On shelves that ranged beside his lone bed's head;
His press was covered with a cloth of red.
And over all there lay a psaltery[7]
Whereon he made an evening's melody,
Playing so sweetly that the chamber rang;
30 And *Angelus ad virginem*[8] he sang;
And after that he warbled the *King's Note*:[9]
Often in good voice was his merry throat.
And thus this gentle clerk his leisure spends
Supported by some income and his friends.
35   This carpenter had lately wed a wife
Whom he loved better than he loved his life;
And she was come to eighteen years of age.
Jealous he was and held her close in cage.
For she was wild and young and he was old,
40 And deemed himself as like to be cuckold.[10]
He knew not Cato,[11] for his lore was rude:
That vulgar man should wed similitude.
A man should wed according to estate,
For youth and age are often in debate.
45 But now, since he had fallen in the snare,
He must endure, like other folk, his care.
       Fair was this youthful wife, and therewithal
As weasel's was her body slim and small.
A girdle wore she, barred and striped, of silk.
50 An apron, too, as white as morning milk
About her loins, and full of many a gore;[12]
White was her smock, embroidered all before
And even behind, her collar round about,
Of coal-black silk, on both sides, in and out;
55 The strings of the white cap upon her head
Were, like her collar, black silk worked with thread;
Her fillet[13] was of wide silk worn full high:
And certainly she had a lickerish[14] eye.
She'd thinned out carefully her eyebrows two,
60 And they were arched and black as any sloe.[15]
She was a far more pleasant thing to see
Than is the newly budded young pear-tree;

And softer than the wool is on a wether.[16]
Down from her girdle hung a purse of leather,
65 Tasselled with silk, with latten[17] beading sown.
In all this world, searching it up and down,
So gay a little doll, I well believe,
Or such a wench, there's no man can conceive.
Far brighter was the brilliance of her hue
70 Than in the Tower[18] the gold coins minted new.
And songs came shrilling from her pretty head
As from a swallow's sitting on a shed.
Therewith she'd dance too, and could play and sham
Like any kid or calf about its dam.[19]
75 Her mouth was sweet as bragget[20] or as mead
Or hoard of apples laid in hay or weed.
Skittish she was as is a pretty colt,
Tall as a staff and straight as cross-bow bolt.
A brooch she wore upon her collar low,
80 As broad as boss of buckler did it show;
Her shoes laced up to where a girl's legs thicken.
She was a primrose, and a tender chicken
For any lord to lay upon his bed,
Or yet for any good yeoman to wed.
85   Now, sir, and then, sir, so befell the case,
That on a day this clever Nicholas
Fell in with this young wife to toy and play,
The while he husband was down Osney way,
Clerks being as crafty as the best of us;
90 And unperceived he caught her by the puss,
Saying: "Indeed, unless I have my will,
For secret love of you, sweetheart, I'll spill."[21]
And held her hard about the hips, and how!—
And said: "O darling, love me, love me now,
95 Or I shall die, and pray that God me save!"
        And she leaped as a colt does in the trave,[22]
And with her head she twisted fast away,
And said: "I will not kiss you, by my fay!
Why, let go," cried she, "let go, Nicholas!
100 Or I will call for help and cry 'alas!'
Do take your hands away, for courtesy!"
        This Nicholas for mercy then did cry,

[16]*ram*

[17]*brass*

[18]*Tower of London*

[19]*mother*

[20]*honeyed ale*

[21]*die*

[22]*pen in which a colt is kept when being fitted for shoes*

And spoke so well, and pressed his cause so fast
that she her love did grant him at the last,

[23]Thomas a Becket

105 And swore her oath, by Saint Thomas of Kent,[23]
that she would be at his command, content,
As soon as opportunity she could spy.
    "My husband is so full of jealousy,
Unless you will await me secretly,

110 I know I'm just as good as dead," said she.
"You must keep all quite hidden in this case."
    "Nay, thereof worry not," said Nicholas,
"A clerk has lazily employed his while
If he cannot a carpenter beguile."

115   And thus they were agreed, and then they swore
To wait a while, as I have said before.
When Nicholas had done thus every whit
And patted her about the loins a bit,
He kissed her sweetly, took his psaltery,

120 And played it fast and made a melody.

[24]church

    Then fell it thus, that to the parish kirk,[24]
The Lord Christ Jesus' own works for to work,
This good wife went, upon a holy day;
Her forehead shone as bright as does the May,

125 So well she'd washed it when she left off work.
    Now there was of that church a parish clerk
The which that bore the name of Absalom.
Curled was his hair, shining like gold, and from
His head spread fanwise in a thick bright mop;

130 'Twas parted straight and even on the top;
His cheek was red, his eyes grey as a goose;

[25]Saint Paul's Cathedral, in London

With Saint Paul's[25] windows cut upon his shoes,
He stood in red hose fitting famously.
And he was clothed full well and properly

135 All in a coat of blue, in which were let
Holes for the lacings, which were fairly set.

[26]church garment

And over all he wore a fine surplice[26]
As white as ever hawthorn spray, and nice.
A merry lad he was, so God me save,

[27] duties often performed by clerks

140 And well could he let blood, cut hair, and shave,[27]
And draw a deed or quitclaim,[28] as might chance.

[28]legal document

In twenty manners could he trip and dance,

After the school that reigned in Oxford,[29] though,

And with his two legs swinging to and fro;

145 And he could play upon a violin;

Thereto he sang in treble voice and thin;

And as well could he play on the guitar.

In all the town no inn was, and no bar,

That he'd not visited to make good cheer,

150 Especially were lively barmaids there.

But, truth to tell, he was a bit squeamish

Of farting and of language haughtyish.

This Absalom, who was so light and gay,

Went with a censer[30] on the holy day,

155 Censing the wives like an enthusiast;

And on them many a loving look he cast,

Especially on this carpenter's goodwife.

To look at her he thought a merry life,

She was so pretty, sweet, and lickerous.

160 I dare well say, if she had been a mouse

And he a cat, he would have mauled her some.

This parish clerk, this lively Absalom

Had in his heart, now, such a love-longing

That from no wife took he an offering;

165 For courtesy, he said, he would take none.

The moon, when it was night, full brightly shone,

And his guitar did Absalom then take,

For in love-watching he'd intent to wake.

And forth he went, jolly and amorous,

170 Until he came unto the carpenter's house

A little after cocks began to crow;

And took his stand beneath a shot-window[31]

That was let into the good wood-wright's wall.

He sang then, in his pleasant voice and small,

175 "Oh now, dear lady, if your will it be,

I pray that you will have some ruth[32] on me,"

The words in harmony with his string-plucking.

This carpenter awoke and heard him sing,

And called unto his wife and said, in sum:

180 "What, Alison! Do you hear Absalom,

Who plays and sings beneath our bedroom wall?"

And she said to her husband, therewithal:

[29]*oldest university in England*

[30]*container for burning church incense*

[31]*shuttered window*

[32]*pity*

"Yes, God knows, John, I hear it, truth to tell."
So this went on; what is there better than well?
185 From day to day this pretty Absalom
So wooed her he was woebegone therefrom.
He lay awake all night and all the day;
He combed his spreading hair and dressed him gay;
By go-betweens and agents, too, wooed he,
190 And swore her loyal page he'd ever be.
He sang as tremulously as nightingale;
He sent her sweetened wine and well-spiced ale
And waffles piping hot out of the fire,
And, she being town-bred, mead for her desire.
195 For some by tricks, and some by long descent.
Once, to display his versatility,
He acted Herod[33] on a scaffold high.
But what availed it him in any case?
She was enamoured so of Nicholas
200 That Absalom might go and blow his horn;
He got naught for his labour but her scorn.
And thus she made of Absalom her ape,
And all his earnestness she made a jape.[34]
For truth is in this proverb, and no lie,
205 Men say well thus: It's always he that's nigh
That makes the absent lover seem a sloth.
For now, though Absalom be wildly wroth,
Because he is so far out of her sight,
This handy Nicholas stands in his light.
210 Now bear you well, you clever Nicholas!
For Absalom may wail and sing "Alas!"
And so it chanced that on a Saturday
This carpenter departed to Osney;
And clever Nicholas and Alison
215 Were well agreed to this effect: anon
This Nicholas should put in play a wile[35]
The simple, jealous husband to beguile;
And if it chanced the game should go a-right,
She was to sleep within his arms all night,
220 For this was his desire, and hers also.
Presently then, and without more ado,
This Nicholas, no longer did he tarry,

[33]*character in a medieval religious play*

[34]*joke*

[35]*trick*

But softly to his chamber did he carry
Both food and drink to last at least a day,
225 Saying that to her husband she should say—
If he should come to ask for Nicholas—
Why, she should say she knew not where he was,
For all day she'd not seen him, far or nigh;
She thought he must have got some malady,
230 Because in vain her maid would knock and call;
He'd answer not, whatever might befall.
    And so it was that all that Saturday
This Nicholas quietly in chamber lay,
And ate and slept, or did what pleased him best,
235 Till Sunday when the sun had gone to rest.
    This simple man with wonder heard the tale,
And marvelled what their Nicholas might ail,
And said: "I am afraid, by Saint Thomas,
That everything's not well with Nicholas.
240 God send he be not dead so suddenly!
This world is most unstable, certainly;
I saw, today, the corpse being borne to kirk
Of one who, but last Monday, was at work.
Go up," said he unto his boy anon,
245 "Call at his door, or knock there with a stone,
Learn how it is and boldly come tell me."
    The servant went up, then, right sturdily,
And at the chamber door, the while he stood,
He cried and knocked as any madman would—
250 "What! How! What do you, Master Nicholay?
How can you sleep through all the livelong day?"
    But all for naught, he never heard a word;
A hole he found, low down upon a board,
Through which the house cat had been wont to creep;
255 And to that hole he stooped, and through did peep,
And finally he ranged him in his sight.
This Nicholas sat gaping there, upright,
As if he'd looked too long at the new moon.
Downstairs he went and told his master soon
260 In what array he'd found this self-same man.
    This carpenter to cross himself began,
And said: "Now help us, holy Frideswide![36]

[36]*patron saint of Oxford*

Little a man can know what shall betide.
This man is fallen, with his astromy,
265 Into some madness or some agony;
I always feared that somehow this would be!
Men should not meddle in God's privity.
Aye, blessed always be the ignorant man,
Whose creed is all he ever has to scan!
270 So fared another clerk with astromy;
He walked into the meadows for to pry
Into the stars, to learn what should befall,
Until into a clay-pit he did fall;
He saw not that. But yet, by Saint Thomas,
275 I'm sorry for this clever Nicholas.
He shall be scolded for his studying,
If not too late, by Jesus, Heaven's King!
     "Get me a staff, that I may pry before,
The while you, Robin, heave against the door.
280 We'll take him from this studying, I guess."
     And on the chamber door, then, he did press.
His servant was a stout lad, if a dunce,
And by the hasp he heaved it up at once;
Upon the floor that portal fell anon.
285 This Nicholas sat there as still as stone,
Gazing, with gaping mouth, straight up in air.
This carpenter thought he was in despair,
And took him by the shoulders, mightily,
And shook him hard, and cried out, vehemently:
290 "What! Nicholay! Why how now! Come, look down!
Awake, and think on Jesus' death and crown!
I cross you from all elves and magic wights!"

37*spell to cast out
dark spirits*

     And then the night-spell[37] said he out, by rights,
At the four corners of the house about,
295 And at the threshold of the door, without:—
     "O Jesus Christ and good Saint Benedict,
Protect this house from all that may afflict,
For the night hag the white Paternoster![38]—
Where hast thou gone, Saint Peter's sister?"

38*usually the Lord's
prayer; in this
case, a prayer
used to drive out
spirits*

300 And at the last this clever Nicholas
Began to sigh full sore, and said: "Alas!
Shall all the world be lost so soon again?"

This carpenter replied: "What say you, then?
What! Think on God, as we do, men that swink."[39]

305   This Nicholas replied: "Go fetch me drink;
And afterward I'll tell you privately
A certain thing concerning you and me;
I'll tell it to no other man or men."

        This carpenter went down and came again,
310 And brought of potent ale a brimming quart;
And when each one of them had drunk his part,
Nicholas shut the door fast, and with that
He drew a seat and near the carpenter sat.

        He said: "Now, John, my good host, lief[10] and dear,
315 You must upon your true faith swear, right here,
That to no man will you this word betray;
For it is Christ's own word that I will say,
And if you tell a man, you're ruined quite;
This punishment shall come to you, of right,
320 That if you're traitor you'll go mad—and should!"

        "Nay, Christ forbid it, for His holy blood!"
Said then this simple man: "I am no blab,
Nor, though I say it, am I fond of gab.
Say what you will, I never will it tell
325 To child or wife, by Him that harried[41] Hell!"

        "Now, John," said Nicholas, "I will not lie;
But I've found out, from my astrology,
As I have looked upon the moon so bright,
That now, come Monday next, at nine of night,
330 Shall fall a rain so wildly mad as would
Have been, by half, greater than Noah's flood.
This world," he said, "in less time than an hour,
Shall all be drowned, so terrible is this shower;
Thus shall all mankind drown and lose all life."

335   This carpenter replied: "Alas, my wife!
And shall she drown? Alas, my Alison!"
For grief of this he almost fell. Anon
He said: "Is there no remedy in this case?"

        "Why yes, good luck," said clever Nicholas,
340 "If you will work by counsel of the wise;
You must not act on what your wits advise.
For so says Solomon,[42] and it's all true,

[39]*toil*

[40]*beloved*

[41]*Jesus*

[42]*wise king in the
Bible*

[43] *regret*

'Work by advice and thou shalt never rue.'[43]
And if you'll act as counselled and not fail,
345 I undertake, without a mast or sail,
To save us all, aye you and her and me.
Haven't you heard of Noah,[44] how saved was he,
Because Our Lord had warned him how to keep
Out of the flood that covered earth so deep?"

[44] *in the Bible, a*
man told by God
to build a boat in
preparation for a
great flood

350   "Yes," said the carpenter, "long years ago."
    "Have you not heard," asked Nicholas, "also
The sorrow of Noah and his fellowship
In getting his wife to go aboard the ship?
He would have rather, I dare undertake,
355 At that time, and for all the weather black,
That she had one ship for herself alone.
Therefore, do you know what would best be done?
This thing needs haste, and of a hasty thing
Men must not preach nor do long tarrying.
360   "Presently go, and fetch here to this inn
A kneading-tub, or brewing vat, and win
One each for us, but see that they are large,
Wherein we may swim out as in a barge,
And have therein sufficient food and drink
365 For one day only; that's enough, I think.
The water will dry up and flow away

[45] *nine a.m.*

About the prime[45] of the succeeding day.
But Robin must not know of this, your knave,
And even Jill, your maid, I may not save;
370 Ask me not why, for though you do ask me,
I will not tell you of God's privity.
Suffice you, then, unless your wits are mad,
To have a great a grace as Noah had.
Your wife I shall not lose, there is no doubt,
375 Go, now, your way, and speedily get about,
But when you have, for you and her and me,
Procured these kneading-tubs, or beer-vats, three,
Then you shall hang them near the roof-tree high,

[46] *preparation*

That no man our purveyance[46] may espy.
380 And when you thus have done, as I have said,
And have put in our drink and meat and bread,
Also an axe to cut the ropes in two

When the flood comes, that we may float and go,
And cut a hole, high up, upon the gable,
385 Upon the garden side, over the stable,
That we may freely pass forth on our way
When the great rain and flood are gone that day—
Then shall you float as merrily, I'll stake,
As does the white duck after the white drake.
390 Then I will call, 'Ho, Alison! Ho, John!
Be cheery, for the flood will pass anon.'
And you will say, 'Hail, Master Nicholay!
Good morn, I see you well, for it is day!'
And then shall we be barons all our life
395 Of all the world, like Noah and his wife.
    "But of one thing I warn you now, outright.
Be well advised, that on that very night
When we have reached our ships and got aboard,
Not one of us must speak or whisper word,
400 Nor call, nor cry, but sit in silent prayer;
For this is God's own bidding, hence—don't dare!
    "Your wife and you must hang apart, that in
The night shall come no chance for you to sin
Either in looking or in carnal deed.
405 These orders I have told you, go, God speed!
Tomorrow night, when all men are asleep,
Into our kneading-tubs will we three creep
And sit there, still, awaiting God's high grace.
Go, now, your way, I have no longer space
410 Of time to make a longer sermoning.
Men say thus: 'Send the wise and say no thing.'
You are so wise it needs not that I teach;
Go, save our lives, and that I do beseech."
    This sill carpenter went on his way.
415 Often he cried "Alas!" and "Welaway!"
And to his wife he told all, privately;
But she was better taught thereof than he
How all this rigmarole[47] was to apply.
Nevertheless she acted as she'd die,
420 And said: "Alas! Go on your way anon,
Help us escape, or we are lost, each one;
I am your true and lawfully wedded wife;

[47] *ridiculous action*

Go, my dear spouse, and help to save our life."
　　Lo, what a great thing is affection found!
425　Men die of imagination, I'll be bound,
　　So deep an imprint may the spirit take.
　　This hapless carpenter began to quake;
　　He thought now, verily, that he could see
　　Old Noah's flood come wallowing like the sea
430　To drown his Alison, his honey dear.
　　He wept, he wailed, he made but sorry cheer,
　　He sighed and made full many a sob and sough.
　　He went and got himself a kneading-trough
　　And, after that, two tubs he somewhere found
435　And to his dwelling privately sent round,
　　And hung them near the roof, all secretly.
　　With his own hand, then, made he ladders three,
　　To climb up by the rungs thereof, it seems,
　　And reach the tubs left hanging to the beams;

[48]*stocked with food*　440　And those he victualled[48] tubs and kneading-trough
　　With bread and cheese and good jugged ale, enough
　　To satisfy the needs of one full day.
　　But ere he'd put all this in such array,
　　He sent his servants, boy and maid, right down
445　Upon some errand into London town.
　　And on the Monday, when it came on night,
　　He shut his door, without a candle-light,
　　And ordered everything as it should be.
　　And shortly after up they climbed, all three;

[49]*about 660 feet*　450　They sat while one might plow a furlong-way.[49]
　　　　"Now, by Our Father, hush!" said Nicholay,
　　And "Hush!" said John, and "Hush!" said Alison.
　　　　This carpenter, his loud devotion done,
　　Sat silent, saying mentally a prayer,
455　And waiting for the rain, to hear it there.
　　　　The deathlike sleep of utter weariness
　　Fell on this wood-wright even (as I guess)
　　About the curfew time, or little more;

[50]*effort*　　For travail[50] of his spirit he groaned sore,
460　And soon he snored, for badly his head lay.
　　Down by the ladder crept his Nicholay,
　　And Alison, right softly down she sped.

Without more words they went and got in bed
Even where the carpenter was wont[51] to lie.
465   There was the revel and the melody!
And thus lie Alison and Nicholas,
In joy that goes by many an alias,
Until the bells for lauds[52] began to ring
And friars to the chancel[53] went to sing.
470   This parish clerk, this amorous Absalom,
Whom love has made so woebegone and dumb,
Upon the Monday was down Osney way,
With company, to find some sport and play;
And there he chanced to ask a cloisterer,
475   Privately, after John the carpenter.
This monk drew him apart, out of the kirk,[54]
And said: "I have not seen him here at work
Since Saturday; I think well that he went
For timber, that the abbot has him sent;
480   For he is wont for timber thus to go,
Remaining at the grange[55] a day or so;
Or else he's surely at his house today;
But which it is I cannot truly say."
      This Absalom right happy was and light,
485   And thought: "Now is the time to wake all night;
For certainly I saw him not stirring
About his door since day began to spring.
So may I thrive, as I shall, at cock's crow,
Knock cautiously upon the window low
490   Which is so placed upon his bedroom wall.
To Alison then will I tell of all
My love-longing, and thus I shall not miss
That at the least I'll have her lips to kiss.
Some sort of comfort shall I have, I say,
495   My mouth's been itching all this livelong day;
That is a sign of kissing at the least.
Al night I dreamed, too, I was at a feast.
Therefore I'll go and sleep two hours away,
And all this night then will I wake and play."
500   And so when time of first cock-crow was come,
Up rose this merry lover, Absalom,
And dressed him gay and all at point-device,[56]

[51]*used*

[52]*pre-dawn church service*

[53]*part of a church containing the choir seats and altar*

[54]*church*

[55]*outer area of a farm*

[56]*carefully; to the last detail*

But first he chewed some licorice and spice
So he'd smell sweet, ere he had combed his hair.

505   Under his tongue some bits of true-love[57] rare,
For thereby thought he to be more gracious.
He went, then, to the carpenter's dark house.
And silent stood beneath the shot-window;
Unto his breast it reached, it was so low;
510   And he coughed softly, in a low half tone:
"What do you, honeycomb, sweet Alison?
My cinnamon, my fair bird, my sweetie,
Awake, O darling mine, and speak to me!
It's little thought you give me and my woe,
515   Who for your love do sweat where'er I go.
Yet it's no wonder that I faint and sweat;
I long as does the lamb for mother's teat.
Truly, sweetheart, I have such love-longing
That like a turtle-dove's my true yearning;
520   And I can eat no more than can a maid."
     "Go from the window, jack-a-napes," she said,
"For, s'help me God, it is not 'come kiss me.'
I love another, or to blame I'd be,
Better than you, by Jesus, Absalom!
525   Go on your way, or I'll stone you therefrom,
And let me sleep, the fiends take you away!"
     "Alas," quoth Absalom, "and welaway!
That true love ever was so ill beset!
But kiss me, since you'll do no more, my pet,
530   For Jesus' love and for the love of me."
     "And will you go, then, on your way?" asked she.
"Yes truly, darling," said this Absalom.
"Then make you ready," said she, "and I'll come!"
And unto Nicholas said she, low and still:
535   "Be silent now, and you shall laugh your fill."
     This Absalom plumped down upon his knees,
And said: "I am a lord in all degrees;
For after this there may be better still!
Darling, my sweetest bird, I wait your will."
540   The window she unbarred, and that in haste.
"Have done," said she, "come on, and do it fast,
Before we're seen by any neighbour's eye."

This Absalom did wipe his mouth all dry;
Dark was the night as pitch, aye dark as coal,
545 And through the window she put out her hole.
And Absalom no better felt nor worse,
But with his mouth he kissed her naked arse
Right greedily, before he knew of this.
Aback he leapt—it seemed somehow amiss,
550 For well he knew a woman has no beard;
He'd felt a thing all rough and longish haired,
And said, "Oh fie, alas! What did I do?"
"Teehee!" she laughed, and clapped the window to;
And Absalom went forth a sorry pace.
555 "A beard! A beard! cried clever Nicholas,
"Now by God's *corpus*,[58] this goes fair and well!"

58*body*

This hapless Absalom, he heard that yell,
And on his lip, for anger, he did bite;
And to himself he said, "I will requite!"
560 Who vigorously rubbed and scrubbed his lips
With dust, with sand, with straw, with cloth, with chips,
But Absalom, and often cried "Alas!
My soul I give now unto Sathanas,
For rather far than own this town," said he,
565 "For this despite, it's well revenged I'd be.
Alas," said he, "from her I never blenched!"[59]

59*turned away*

His hot love was grown cold, aye and all quenched;
For, from the moment that he'd kissed her arse,
For paramours he didn't care a curse,
570 For he was healed of all his malady;
Indeed all paramours he did defy,
And wept as does a child that has been beat.
With silent step he went across the street
Unto a smith whom men called Sir Jarvis,
575 Who in his smithy forged plow parts, that is
He sharpened shares[60] and coulters[61] busily.

60*plowshares*

61*cutting blades of plows*

This Absalom he knocked all easily,
And said, "Unbar here, Jarvis, for I come."
"What! Who are you?"
                                    "It's I, it's Absalom."
580 "What! Absalom! For Jesus Christ's sweet tree,
Why are you up so early? *Ben'cite!*[62]

62*benecite, standard greeting of goodwill*

63 9th-century monk
supposed to have
advised the king
to found Oxford
University

64 flax on his spin-
ning staff (i.e.,
business to attend
to)

What ails you now, man? Some gay girl, God knows,
Has brought you on the jump to my bellows;
585 By Saint Neot,63 you know well what I mean."
      This Absalom cared not a single bean
For all this play, nor one word back he gave;
He'd more tow on his distaff,64 had this knave,
Than Jarvis knew, and said he: "Friend so dear,
590 This red-hot coulter in the fireplace here,
Lend it to me, I have a need for it,
And I'll return it after just a bit."
      Jarvis replied: "Certainly, were it gold
Or a purse filled with yellow coins untold,
595 Yet should you have it, as I am true smith;
But eh, Christ's foe! What will you do therewith?
      "Let that," said Absalom, "be as it may;
I'll tell you all tomorrow, when it's day"—
And caught the coulter then by the cold steel
600 And softly from the smithy door did steal
And went again up to the wood-wright's wall.
He coughed at first, and then he knocked withal
Upon the window, as before, with care.
      This Alison replied: "Now who is there?
605 And who knocks so? I'll warrant it's a thief."
      "Why no," quoth he, "God knows, my sweet rose-leaf,
I am your Absalom, my own darling!
Of gold," quoth he, "I have brought you a ring;
My mother gave it me, as I'll be saved;
610 Fine gold it is, and it is well engraved;
This will I give you for another kiss."
      This Nicholas had risen for a piss,
And thought that it would carry on the jape
To have his arse kissed by this jack-a-nape.
615 And so he opened window hastily,
And put his arse out thereat, quietly,
Over the buttocks, showing the whole bum;
And thereto said this clerk, this Absalom,
"O speak, sweet bird, I know not where thou art."
620 This Nicholas just then let fly a fart
As loud as it had been a thunder-clap,
And well-nigh blinded Absalom, poor chap;

But he was ready with his iron hot
And Nicholas right in the arse he got.
625   Off went the skin and hand's-breath broad, about,
The coulter burned his bottom so, throughout,
That for the pain he thought that he should die.
And like one mad he started in to cry,
"Help! Water! Water! Help! For God's dear heart!"
630   This carpenter out of his sleep did start,
Hearing that "Water!" cried as madman would,
And thought, "Alas, now comes down Noel's[65] flood!"
He struggled up without another word
And with his axe he cut in two the cord,
635 And down went all; he did not stop to trade
In bread or ale till he'd the journey made,
And there upon the floor he swooning lay.
    Up started Alison and Nicholay
And shouted "Help!" and "Hello!" down the street.
640 The neighbors, great and small, with hastening feet
Swarmed in the house to stare upon this man,
Who lay yet swooning, and all pale and wan;
For in the falling he had smashed his arm.
He had to suffer, too, another harm,
645 For when he spoke he was at once borne down
By clever Nicholas and Alison.
For they told everyone that he was odd;[66]
He was so much afraid of "Noel's" flood,
Through fantasy, that out of vanity
650 He'd gone and bought these kneading-tubs, all three,
And that he'd hung them near the roof above;
And that he had prayed them, for God's dear love,
To sit with him and bear him company.
    The people laughed at all this fantasy;
655 Up to the roof they looked, and there did gape,
And so turned all his injury to a jape.
For when this carpenter got in a word,
'Twas all in vain, no man his reasons heard;
With oaths impressive he was so sworn down
660 That he was held for mad by all the town;
For every clerk did side with every other.
They said: "The man is crazy, my dear brother."

[65]*Noah's*

[66]*crazy*

And everyone did laugh at all this strife.

Thus futtered[67] was the carpenter's goodwife,

665 For all his watching and his jealousy;

And Absalom has kissed her nether eye;

And Nicholas is branded on the butt.

This tale is done, and God save all the rout.[68]

[68]*crowd*

The Wife of Bath's
P R O L O G U E

'NOW WILL I tell you truth, by Saint Thomas[1]
Of why I tore from out his book a leaf
For which he struck me so it made me deaf.
   "He had a book that gladly, night and day
5 For his amusement he would read always.
Called 'Theophrastus' and 'Valeriou',[2]
At which book would he laugh uproarious
And every night and day 'twas his custom,
When he had leisure and took some vacation
10 From all his other worldly occupation,
To read, within this book, of wicked wives.
He knew of them more legends and more lives
Than are of good wives written in the Bible.
For trust me well, it is impossible
15 That any cleric shall speak well of wives,
Unless it be of saints and holy lives,
But naught for other women will they do.
By God, if women had but written stories,
As have these clerks within their oratories,
20 They would have written of men more wickedness
Than all the race of Adam could redress.
Therefore no woman by a clerk is praised.

A clerk, when he is old and can naught do
Of Venus' labours worth his worn-out shoe,

25 Then sits he down and writes, in his dotage,[3]
That women cannot keep vow of marriage!
    "But now to tell you, as I started to,
Why I was beaten for a book, pardieu.
Upon a night Jenkin, who was our sire,[4]

30 Read in his book, as he sat by the fire,
Of Mother Eve who, by her wickedness,
First brought mankind to all his wretchedness
For which Lord Jesus Christ Himself was slain,
Who, with His heart's blood, saved us thus again.
35 Lo, here plainly of woman may you find
That woman was the ruin of mankind.
Then read he out how Samson[5] lost his hairs

When sleeping, his mistress cut them with her shears;
And through this treason lost he either eye.
40 And nothing escaped him of the pain and woe
That Socrates[6] had with his spouses two;"

"Of Clytemnestra,[7] for her lechery,
Who caused her husband's death by treachery,
He read all thus with greatest zest, I vow.

45 "Of Livia[8] and Lucia[9] told he me,
For both of them their husbands killed, you see,
The one for love, the other killed for hate;
Then did he tell how one Latumius

Complained unto his comrade Arrius

50 That in his garden grew a baleful tree
Whereon, he said, his wives, and they were three,
Had hanged themselves for wretchedness and woe.
'Dear brother,' Arrius said, 'and did they so?
Give me a graft of that same blessed tree
55 And in my garden planted it shall be!'
Of wives of later date he also read,
How some had slain their husbands in their bed
And let their lovers shag them all the night
While corpses lay upon the floor upright.
60 And some had driven nails into the brain
While husbands slept and in such wise were slain.
And some had given them poison in their drink.

He told more evil than the mind can think.
And therewithal he knew of more proverbs
65 Than in this world there grows of grass or herbs.
'Better,' he said, 'your habitation be
With lion wild or dragon foul,' said he,
'Than with a woman who will nag and chide.'
'Better,' he said, 'on the housetop abide
70 Than with a brawling wife down in the house;
Such are so wicked and contrarious
They hate the thing their husband loves, for aye.'
And when I saw he'd never make an end
Of reading in this cursed book at night,
75 Three leaves of it I snatched and tore outright
Out of his book, right as he read; also
Upon the cheek I gave him such a blow
That in our fire he reeled and fell right down.
Then he got up as does a wild lion,
80 And with his fist he struck me on the head,
And on the floor I lay as I were dead.
And when he saw how limp and still I lay,
He was afraid and would have run away,
Until at last out of my swoon I made:
85 'Oh, have you slain me, you false thief?' I said,
'And for my land have you thus murdered me?
Kiss me before I die, and let me be.'"

      "He came to me and near me he knelt down,
And said: 'O my dear sister Alison,
90 So help me God, I'll never strike you more;
What I have done, you are to blame therefor.
But all the same, forgiveness now I seek!'
And thereupon I hit him on the cheek,
And said: 'Thief, so much vengeance do I wreak
95 Now will I die, I can no longer speak!'
But at the last, and with much care and woe,
We made it up between ourselves. And so
He put the bridle reins within my hand
To have the governing of house and land;
100 And of his tongue and of his hand, also;
And I made him burn his book, right then, oho!
And when I had thus gathered unto me

By mastery all sovereignty,
And he had said: 'My own true wedded wife,
105 Do as you please the term of all your life;
Keep your honor, and also my estate'—
After that day we never had debate.
God help me so, I was to him as kind
As any wife from Denmark unto Inde,
110 And also true, and so was he to me.
I pray to God, that sits in majesty,
So bless his soul for all his mercy dear.
Now will I say my tale, if you will hear."

THE TALE OF THE
Wife of Bath

NOW IN THE OLDEN days of King Arthur,[1]
Of whom the Britons speak with great honour,
All this wide land was land of faery.
The elf-queen, with her jolly company,
5 Danced oftentimes on many a green mead;[2]
This was the old opinion, as I read.
But now no man can see the elves, you know.
For now the so-great charity and prayers
Of limiters and other holy friars
10 That do infest each land and every stream
As thick as motes are in a bright sunbeam,
Blessing halls, chambers, kitchens, ladies' bowers,
Cities and towns and castles and high towers,
Villages, barns, cowsheds and dairies—
15 This causes it that there are now no fairies.
For where was wont to walk full many an elf,
Right there walks now the limiter himself
In both the later and early mornings,
Saying his matins[3] and such holy things,
20 As he goes round his district in his gown.
Women may now go safely up and down,
In every copse or under every tree;

[1] *legendary British king*

[2] *meadow*

[3] *morning prayers*

[4]*evil spirit which
preyed on women
sexually*

There is no other incubus[4] than he,
And would do them naught but dishonour.

25   And so befell it that this King Arthur
Had at his court a lusty bachelor
Who, on a day, came riding from river;
And happened that, alone as she was born,
He saw a maiden walking through the corn,

30   From whom, in spite of all she did and said,
Straightway by force he took her maidenhead;
For which violation was there such clamour,
And such appealing unto King Arthur,
That soon condemned was this knight to be dead

35   By course of law, and should have lost his head,
Peradventure, such being the statute then;
But that the other ladies and the queen
So long prayed of the king to show him grace,
He granted life, at last, in the law's place,

40   And gave him to the queen, as she should will,
Whether she'd save him, or his blood should spill.

        The queen she thanked the king with all her might,
And after this, thus spoke she to the knight,
When she'd an opportunity, one day:

45   "You stand yet," said she, "in such poor a way
That for your life you've no security.
I'll grant you life if you can tell to me
What thing it is that women most desire.
Be wise, and keep your neck from iron dire!

50   And if you cannot tell it me anon,
Then will I give you license to be gone
A twelvemonth and a day, to search and learn
Sufficient answer in this grave concern.
And your knight's word I'll have, ere forth you pace,

55   To yield your body to me in this place."

        And so he took his leave and went his way.
He sought out every house and every place
Wherein he hoped to find that he had grace
To learn what women love the most of all;

60   But nowhere ever did it him befall
To find, upon the question stated here,
Two persons who agreed with statement clear.

Some said that women all loved best riches,
Some said, fair fame, and some said, prettiness;
65 Some, rich array, some said 'twas lust abed
And often to be widowed and re-wed.
Some said that our poor hearts are aye most eased
When we have been most flattered and thus pleased.
And he went near the truth, I will not lie;
70 A man may win us best with flattery;
And with attentions and with busyness
We're often limed,[5] the greater and the less.  [5]*caught*
And some folk say that great delight have we
To be held constant, also trustworthy,
75 And on one purpose steadfastly to dwell,
And not betray a thing that men may tell.
But that tale is not worth a rake's handle,
For God knows, we women can no thing conceal.
When what the knight went for he could not find out,
80 That is, the thing that women love the best,
Most saddened was the spirit in his breast;
But home he goes, he could no more delay.
The day was come when home he turned his way;
And on his way it chanced that he should ride
85 In all his care, beneath a forest's side,
And there he saw, a-dancing him before,
Full four and twenty ladies, maybe more;
Toward which dance eagerly did he turn
In hope that there some wisdom he should learn.
90 But truly, ere he came upon them there,
The dancers vanished all, he knew not where.
No creature saw he that gave sign of life,
Save, on the greensward sitting, an old wife;
A fouler person could no man devise.
95 Before the knight this old wife did arise,
And said: "Sir knight, hence lies no travelled way.
Tell me what thing you seek, and by your fay,[6] [6]*faith*
Perchance you'll find it may the better be;
These ancient folk know many things," said she.
100 "Dear mother," said this knight assuredly
"I am but dead, save I can tell, truly,
What thing it is that women most desire;

Could you inform me, I'd pay well your hire."

"Plight[7] me your troth[8] here, hand in hand," said she,

105 "That you will do, whatever it may be,

The thing I ask if it lie in your might;

And I'll give you your answer ere the night."

"Have here my word," said he. "That thing I grant."

"Then," said the crone, "of this I make my vaunt,

110 Your life is safe; and I will stand thereby,

Upon my life, the queen will say as I.

Let's see which is the proudest of them all

That wears upon her hair kerchief or caul,[9]

Shall dare say no to that which I shall teach;

115 Let us go now and without longer speech."

Then whispered she a sentence in his ear,

And bade him to be glad and have no fear.

When they were come unto the court, this knight

Said he had kept his promise as was right,

120 And ready was his answer, as he said.

Full many a noble wife, and many a maid,

And many a widow, since they are so wise,

The queen herself sitting as high justice,

Assembled were, his answer there to hear;

125 And then the knight was bidden to appear.

Command was given for silence in the hall,

And that the knight should tell before them all

What thing all worldly women love the best.

This knight did not stand dumb, as does a beast,

130 But to this question presently answered

With manly voice, so that the whole court heard:

"My liege[10] lady, generally," said he,

"Women desire to have the sovereignty

As well upon their husband as their love,

135 And to have mastery their man above;

This thing you most desire, though me you kill

Do as you please, I am here at your will."

In all the court there was no wife or maid

Or widow that denied the thing he said,

140 But all held, he was worthy to have life.

And with that word up started the old wife

Whom he had seen a-sitting on the green.

[7]*pledge*

[8]*vow*

[9]*hairnet*

[10]*superior*

"Mercy," cried she, "my sovereign lady queen!
Before the court's dismissed, give me my right.
145 'Twas I who taught the answer to this knight;
For which he did plight troth to me, out there,
That the first thing I should of him require
He would do that, if it lay in his might.
Before the court, now, pray I you, sir knight,"
150 Said she, "that you will take me for your wife;
For well you know that I have saved your life.
If this be false, say nay, upon your fay!"
   This knight replied: "Alas and welaway!
That I so promised I will not protest.
155 But for God's love pray make a new request,
Take all my wealth and let my body go."
   "Nay then," said she, "beshrew us if I do!
For though I may be foul and old and poor,
I will not, for all metal and all ore
160 That from the earth is dug or lies above,
Be aught except your wife and your true love."
   "My love?" cried he, "nay, rather my damnation!
Alas! that any of my race and station
Should ever so dishonoured foully be!"
165   But all for naught; the end was this, that he
Was so constrained he needs must go and wed,
And take his ancient wife and go to bed.
   Great was the woe the knight had in his thought
When he, with her, to marriage bed was brought;
170 He rolled about and turned him to and fro.
His old wife lay there, always smiling so,
And said: "O my dear husband, ben'cite!
Fares every knight with wife as you with me?
Is this the custom in King Arthur's house?
175 Are knights of his all so fastidious?
I am your own true love and, more, your wife;
And I am she who saved your very life;
And truly, since I've never done you wrong,
Why do you treat me so, this first night long?
180 You act as does a man who's lost his wit;
What is my fault? For God's love tell me it,
And it shall be amended, if I may."

"Amended!" cried this knight, "Alas, nay, nay!
It will not be amended ever, no!
185 You are so loathsome, and so old also,
And therewith of so low a race were born,
It's little wonder that I toss and turn.
Would God my heart would break within my breast!"
      "Is this," asked she, "the cause of your unrest?"
190 "Yes, truly," said he, "and no wonder 'tis."
      "Now, sir," said she, "I could amend all this,
If I but would, and that within days three,
If you would bear yourself well towards me.
But since you speak of such gentility
195 As is descended from old wealth, till ye
Claim that for that you should be gentlemen,
I hold such arrogance not worth a hen.
Find him who is most virtuous alway,
Alone or publicly, and most tries aye
200 To do whatever noble deeds he can,
And take him for the greatest gentleman.
Christ wills we claim of Him our nobleness,
Not of our elders, for their old riches.
      "And when you me reproach for poverty,
205 The High God, in Whom we believe, say I,
In voluntary poverty lived His life.
And surely every man, or maid, or wife
May understand that Jesus, Heaven's King,
Would not have chosen vileness of living.
210 Glad poverty's an honest thing, that's plain,
Which Seneca[11] and other clerks maintain.
Whoso will be content with poverty,
I hold him rich, though not a shirt has he.
And he that covets much is a poor wight,
215 For he would gain what's all beyond his might.
But he that has not, nor desires to have,
Is rich, although you hold him but a knave."
      "Now since you say that I am foul and old,
Then fear you not to be made of a cuckold;[12]
220 For dirt and age, as prosperous I may be,
Are mighty wardens over chastity.
Nevertheless, since I know your delight,

[11]Roman author admired for his views on morality and upright living

[12]man cheated on by his wife

I'll satisfy your wordly appetite."
   "Choose, now," said she, "one of these two things, aye,
225 To have me foul and old until I die,
And be to you a true and humble wife,
And never anger you in all my life;
Or else to have me young and very fair
And take your chance with those who will repair
230 Unto your house, and all because of me,
Or in some other place, as well may be.
Now choose which you like better and reply."
   This knight considered, and did sorely sigh,
But at the last replied as you shall hear:
235 "My lady and my love, and wife so dear,
I put myself in your wise governing;
Do you choose which may be the more pleasing,
And bring most honour to you, and me also.
I care not which it be of these things two;
240 For if you like it, that suffices me."
   "Then have I got of you the mastery,
Since I may choose and govern, in earnest?"
   "Yes, truly, wife," said he, "I hold that best."
   "Kiss me," said she, "we'll be no longer wroth,
245 For by my truth, to you I will be both;
That is to say, I'll be both good and fair.
I pray God I go mad, and so declare,
If I be not to you as good and true
As ever wife was since the world was new.
250 And, save I be, at dawn, as fairly seen
As any lady, empress, or great queen
That is between the east and the far west,
Do with my life and death as you like best.
Throw back the curtain and see how it is."
255   And when the knight saw verily all this,
That she so very fair was, and young too,
For joy he clasped her in his strong arms two,
His heart bathed in a bath of utter bliss;
A thousand times, all in a row, he'd kiss.
260 And she obeyed his wish in everything.
   And thus they lived unto their lives' fair end,
In perfect joy; and Jesus to us send

Meek husbands, and young ones, fresh in bed,
And good luck to outlive them that we wed.

265 And I pray Jesus to cut short the lives
Of those who'll not be governed by their wives;
And old and querulous[13] niggards[14] with their pence,
And send them soon a mortal pestilence!

[13]*irritable*

[14]*misers*

The Pardoner's
T A L E

IN FLANDERS, once, there was a company
Of young companions given to folly,
Riot and gambling, brothels and taverns;
And, to the music of harps, lutes, gitterns,[1]
5 They danced and played at dice both day and night,
And ate also and drank beyond their might,
Whereby they made the devil's sacrifice
Within that devil's temple, wicked wise,
By superfluity both vile and vain.
10 So damnable their oaths and so profane
That it was terrible to hear them swear;
Our blessed Saviour's Body did they tear;
They thought the Jews[2] had rent Him not enough;
And each of them at others' sins would laugh.
15 Then entered dancing-girls of ill repute,
Graceful and slim, and girls who peddled fruit,
Harpers and bawds[3] and women selling cake,
Who do their office for the Devil's sake,
To kindle and blow the fire of lechery,
20 Which is so closely joined with gluttony;
I call on holy writ, now, to witness
That lust is in all wine and drunkenness.

[1]guitars

[2]Jews had been
expelled from
England in 1290,
but were still a
major source of
fascination for
English Christians

[3]loose women

O gluttony, of you we may complain!
Oh, knew a man how many maladies
25 Follow on excess and on gluttonies,
Surely he would be then more moderate
In diet, and at table more sedate.
Alas! A foul thing is it, by my fay,
To speak this word, and fouler is the deed,
30 When man so guzzles of the white and red
That of his own throat makes he his privy,
Because of this cursed superfluity.
But truly, he that such delights entice
Is dead while yet he wallows in this vice.
35 A lecherous thing is wine, and drunkenness
Is full of striving and of wretchedness.
O drunken man, disfigured is your face,
Sour is your breath, foul are you to embrace,
You fall down just as if you were stuck swine;
40 Your tongue is loose, your honest care obscure;
For drunkenness is very sepulture[4]
Of any mind a man may chance to own.
In whom strong drink has domination shown
He can no counsel keep for any dread.
45 Now keep you from the white and from the red.
    And now that I have told of gluttony,
I'll take up gambling, showing you thereby
The curse of chance, and all its evils treat;
From it proceeds false swearing and deceit,
50 Blaspheming, murder, and—what's more—the waste
Of time and money; add to which, debased
And shamed and lost to honour quite is he,
Who once a common gambler's known to be.
And ever the higher one is of estate,
55 The more he's held disgraced and desolate.
And if a prince plays similar hazardry
In all his government and policy,
He loses in the estimate of men
His good repute, and finds it not again.
60 Now these three roisterers,[5] whereof I tell,
Long before prime[6] was rung by any bell,
Were sitting in a tavern for to drink;

[4]*tomb*

[5]*partyers*

[6]*nine a.m.*

And as they sat they heard a small bell clink
Before a corpse being carried to his grave;
65 Whereat one of them called unto his knave:
"Go run," said he, "and ask them civilly
What corpse it is that's just now passing by,
And see that you report the man's name well."
     "Sir," said the boy, "it needs not that they tell.
70 I learned it, ere you came here, full two hours;
He was, by gad, an old comrade of yours;
And he was slain, all suddenly, last night,
When drunk, as he sat on his bench upright;
An unseen thief, called Death, came stalking by,
75 Who hereabouts makes all the people die,
And with his spear he clove his heart in two
And went his way and made no more ado.
He's slain a thousand with this pestilence;
And, master, ere you come in his presence,
80 It seems to me to be right necessary
To be forewarned of such an adversary:
Be ready to meet him for evermore.
My mother taught me this, I say no more."
     "By holy Mary," said the innkeeper,
85 "The boy speaks truth, for Death has slain, this year,
A mile or more hence, in a large village,
Both man and woman, child and hind and page.
I think his habitation must be there;
To be advised of him great wisdom 'twere,
90 Before he did a man some dishonour."
     "Yea, by God's arms!" exclaimed this roisterer,
"Is it such peril, then, this Death to meet?
I'll seek him in the road and in the street,
As I now vow to God's own noble bones!
95 Hear, comrades, we're of one mind, as each owns;
Let each of us hold up his hand to other
And each of us become the other's brother,
And we three will go slay this traitor Death;
He shall be slain who's stopped so many a breath,
100 By God's great dignity, ere it be night."
Together did these three their pledges plight
To live and die, each of them for the other,

As if he were his very own blood brother.
And up they started, drunken, in this rage,
105   And forth they went, and towards that village
Whereof the innkeeper had told before.
And so, with many a grisly oath, they swore
And Jesus' blessed body once more rent—
"Death shall be dead if we find where he went."
110   When they had gone not fully half a mile,
Just as they would have trodden over a stile,
An old man, and a poor , with them did meet.
This ancient man full meekly them did greet,
And said thus: "Now, lords, God keep you and see!"
115   The one that was most insolent of these three
Replied to him: "What? Churl of evil grace,
Why are you all wrapped up, except your face?
Why do you live so long in so great age?"
          This ancient man looked upon his visage
120   And thus replied: "Because I cannot find
A man, nay, though I walked from here to Ind,
Either in town or country who'll engage
To give his youth in barter for my age;
And therefore must I keep my old age still,
125   As long a time as it shall be God's will.
Not even Death, alas! my life will take;
Thus restless I my wretched way must make
But, sirs, in you it is no courtesy
To speak to an old man despitefully,
130   Unless in word he trespass or in deed.
In holy writ you may, yourselves, well read
'Before an old man, hoar⁷ upon the head,
You should arise.' Which I advise you read,
Nor to an old man any injury do
135   More than you would that men should do to you
In age, if you so long time shall abide;
And God be with you, whether you walk or ride.
I must pass on now where I have to go."
          "Nay, ancient churl, by God it sha'n't be so,"
140   Cried out this other hazarder, anon;
"You sha'n't depart so easily, by Saint John!
You spoke just now of that same traitor Death,

⁷white

Who in this country stops our good friends' breath
Hear my true word, since you are his own spy,
145 Tell where he is or you shall rue it, aye
By God and by the holy Sacrament!
Indeed you must be, with this Death, intent
To slay all us young people, you false thief."
    "Now, sirs," said he, "if you're so keen, in brief,
150 to find out Death, turn up this crooked way,
For in that grove I left him, by my fay,
Under a tree, and there he will abide;
Nor for your boasts will he a moment hide.
See you that oak? Right there you shall him find.
155 God save you, Who redeemed all humankind,
And mend your ways!"—thus said this ancient man.
And every one of these three roisterers ran
Till he came to that tree; and there they found,
Of florins[8] of fine gold, new-minted, round,
160 Well-nigh eight bushels full, or so they thought.
No longer, then, after this Death they sought,
But each of them so glad was of that sight,
Because the florins were so fair and bright,
That down they all sat by this precious hoard.
165 The worst of them was first to speak a word.
"Brothers," said he, "take heed to what I say;
My wits are keen, although I mock and play.
This treasure here Fortune to us has given
That mirth and jollity our lives may liven,
170 And easily as it's come, so will we spend.
But might this gold be carried from this place
Home to my house, or if you will, to yours—
For well we know that all this gold is ours—
Then were we all in high felicity.
175 But certainly by day this may not be;
For men would say that we were robbers strong,
And we'd, for our own treasure, hang ere long.
This treasure must be carried home by night
All prudently and slyly, out of sight.
180 So I propose that cuts among us all
Be drawn, and let's see where the cut will fall;
And he that gets the short cut, blithe of heart

[8]*coins*

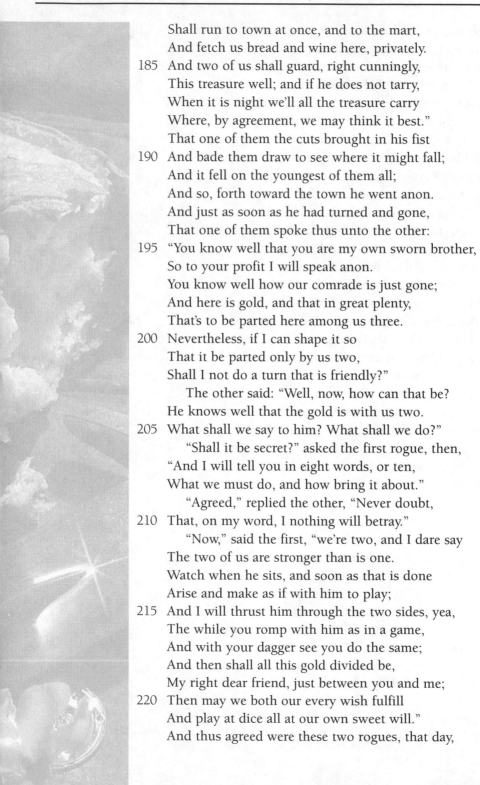

Shall run to town at once, and to the mart,
And fetch us bread and wine here, privately.
185 And two of us shall guard, right cunningly,
This treasure well; and if he does not tarry,
When it is night we'll all the treasure carry
Where, by agreement, we may think it best."
That one of them the cuts brought in his fist
190 And bade them draw to see where it might fall;
And it fell on the youngest of them all;
And so, forth toward the town he went anon.
And just as soon as he had turned and gone,
That one of them spoke thus unto the other:
195 "You know well that you are my own sworn brother,
So to your profit I will speak anon.
You know well how our comrade is just gone;
And here is gold, and that in great plenty,
That's to be parted here among us three.
200 Nevertheless, if I can shape it so
That it be parted only by us two,
Shall I not do a turn that is friendly?"
      The other said: "Well, now, how can that be?
He knows well that the gold is with us two.
205 What shall we say to him? What shall we do?"
      "Shall it be secret?" asked the first rogue, then,
"And I will tell you in eight words, or ten,
What we must do, and how bring it about."
      "Agreed," replied the other, "Never doubt,
210 That, on my word, I nothing will betray."
      "Now," said the first, "we're two, and I dare say
The two of us are stronger than is one.
Watch when he sits, and soon as that is done
Arise and make as if with him to play;
215 And I will thrust him through the two sides, yea,
The while you romp with him as in a game,
And with your dagger see you do the same;
And then shall all this gold divided be,
My right dear friend, just between you and me;
220 Then may we both our every wish fulfill
And play at dice all at our own sweet will."
And thus agreed were these two rogues, that day,

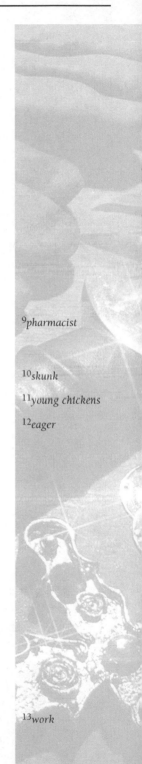

To slay the third, as you have heard me say.
   This youngest rogue who'd gone into the town,
225 Often in fancy rolled he up and down
The beauty of those florins new and bright.
"O Lord," thought he, "if so be that I might
Have all this treasure to myself alone,
There is no man who lives beneath the throne
230 Of God that should be then so merry as I."
   And at the last the Fiend, our enemy,
Put in his thought that he should poison buy
With which he might kill both his fellows; aye,
The Devil found him in such wicked state,
235 He had full leave his grief to consummate;
For it was utterly the man's intent
To kill them both and never to repent.
And on he strode, no longer would he tarry,
Into the town, to an apothecary,[9]

[9]*pharmacist*

240 And prayed of him that he'd prepare and sell
Some poison for his rats, and some as well
For a polecat[10] that in his yard had lain,

[10]*skunk*

The which, he said, his capons[11] there had slain,

[11]*young chickens*

And fain[12] he was to rid him, if he might,

[12]*eager*

245 Of vermin that thus damaged him by night.
The apothecary said: "And you shall have
A thing of which, so God my spirit save,
In all this world there is not live creature
That's eaten or has drunk of this mixture
250 As much as equals but a grain of wheat,
That shall not sudden death thereafter meet;
Yea, die he shall, and in a shorter while
Than you require to walk but one short mile;
This poison is so violent and strong."
255 This wicked man the poison took along
With him boxed up, and then he straightway ran
Into the street adjoining, to a man,
And of him borrowed generous bottles three;
And into two his poison then poured he;
260 The third one he kept clean for his own drink.
For all that night he was resolved to swink[13]

[13]*work*

In carrying the florins from that place.

And when this roisterer, with evil grace,
Had filled with wine his mighty bottles three,
265   Then to his comrades forth again went he.
What is the need to tell about it more?
For just as they had planned his death before,
Just so they murdered him, and that anon.
And when the thing was done, then spoke the one:
270   "Now let us sit and drink and so be merry,
And afterward we will his body bury."
And as he spoke, one bottle of the three
He took wherein the poison chanced to be
And drank and gave his comrade drink also,
275   For which, and that anon, lay dead these two.
Thus ended these two homicides in woe;
Died thus the treacherous poisoner also.
O cursed sin, full of abominableness!
O treacherous homicide! O wickedness!
280   O gluttony, lechery, and hazardry!
O blasphemer of Christ with villainy,
And with great oaths, habitual for pride!
Alas! Mankind, how may this thing betide[14]

[14]*happen*

That to thy dear Creator, Who thee wrought,
285   And with His precious blood salvation bought,
Thou art so false and so unkind, alas!
Now, good men, God forgive you each trespass,
And keep you from the sin of avarice.[15]

[15]*eagerness for money; greed*

My holy pardon cures and will suffice,
290   So that it brings me gold, or silver brings,
Or else, I care not—brooches, spoons or rings.
Bow down your heads before this holy bull!
Come up, you wives, and offer of your wool!
Your names I'll enter on my roll, anon,
295   And into Heaven's bliss you'll go, each one.
For I'll absolve you, by my special power,
You that make offering, as clean this hour
As you were born.
     And lo, sirs, thus I preach.

[16]*healer*

300   And Jesus Christ, who is our souls' great leech,[16]
So grant you each his pardon to receive;
For that is best; I will not you deceive.

But, sirs, one word forgot I in my tale;
I've relics in my pouch that cannot fail,
305 As good as England ever saw, I hope,
The which I got by kindness of the pope.
If gifts your change of heart and mind reveal.
You'll get my absolution while you kneel.
Come forth, and kneel down here before, anon.
310 And humbly you'll receive my full pardon;
Or else receive a pardon as you wend,
All new and fresh as every mile shall end,
So that you offer me each time, anew,
More gold and silver, all good coins and true.
315 It is an honour to each one that's here
That you may have a competent pardoner
To give you absolution as you ride,
For all adventures that may still betide.
Perchance from horse may fall down one or two,
320 Breaking his neck, and it might well be you.
See what insurance, then, it is for all
That I within your fellowship did fall,
Who may absolve you, both the great and less,
When soul from body passes, as I guess.
325 I think our host might just as well begin,
For he is most enveloped in all sin.
Come forth, sir host, and offer first anon,
And you shall kiss the relics, every one,
Aye, for a groat!¹⁷ Unbuckle now your purse."

¹⁷*coin*

330 "Nay, nay," said he, "then may I have Christ's curse!
Why, you would have me kissing your old breeches,
And swear they were the relics of a saint,
Though with your excrement 'twere dabbed like paint.
By cross Saint Helen found in Holy Land,
335 I would I had your ballocks in my hand
Instead of relics in a reliquary;
Let's cut them off, and them I'll help you carry;
They shall be shrined within a hog's fat turd."
This pardoner, he answered not a word;
340 So wrathy¹⁸ was he no word would he say.
     "Now," said our host, "I will no longer play
With you, nor any other angry man."

¹⁸*angry*

But at this point the worthy knight began,
When that he saw how all the folk did laugh:
345 "No more of this, for it's gone far enough;
Sir pardoner, be glad and merry here;
And you, sir host, who are to me so dear,
I pray you that you kiss the pardoner.
And, pardoner, I pray you to draw near,
350 And as we did before, let's laugh and play."
And then they kissed and rode forth on their way.

The Nun's Priest's

P R O L O G U E

"HOLD!" cried the knight. "Good sir, no more of this,[1]
What you have said is right enough, and is
Very much more; a little heaviness
Is plenty for the most of us, I guess.

5 For me, I say it's saddening, if you please,
As to men who've enjoyed great wealth and ease,
To hear about their sudden fall, alas,
But the contrary's joy and great solace,
As when a man has been in poor estate

10 And he climbs up and waxes fortunate,
And there abides in all prosperity.
Such things are gladsome, as it seems to me,
And of such things it would be good to tell."
      "Yea, quoth our host, "and by Saint Paul's[2] great bell,

15 You say the truth; this monk, his clapper's loud.
Sir monk, no more of this, so God you bless!
Your tale annoys the entire company;
Sir, tell a tale of hunting now, I pray."
Such things are gladsome, as it seems to me,

20 And of such things it would be good to tell."
      "Nay," said this monk, "I have no wish to play;
Now let another tell, as I have told."

[1]*The monk has just finished giving different examples of the fall of great men.*

[2]*major cathedral in London*

Then spoke our host out, in rude speech and bold,
And said he unto the nun's priest anon:
25 "Come near, you priest, come hither, you Sir John,
Tell us a thing to make our hearts all glad;
Be blithe, although you ride upon a jade.
What though your horse may be both foul and lean?
If he but serves you, why, don't care a bean;
30 Just see your heart is always merry. So."
    "Yes, sir," said he, "yes, host, so may I go,
For, save I'm merry, I know I'll be blamed."
And right away his story has he framed,
And thus he said unto us, every one,
35 This dainty priest, this goodly man, Sir John.

The Nun's Priest's
T A L E

OF THE COCK AND HEN:
CHANTICLEER AND PERTELOTE

A WIDOW poor, somewhat advanced in age,
Lived, on a time, within a small cottage
Beside a grove and standing down a dale.
This widow, now, of whom I tell my tale,
5 Since that same day when she'd been last a wife,
Had led, with patience, her straight simple life,
For she'd small goods and little income-rent;
By husbanding[1] of such as God had sent
She kept herself and her young daughters twain.
10 Three large sows had she, and no more, 'tis pain,
Three cows and a lone sheep that she called Moll.
Right sooty was her bedroom and her hall,
Wherein she'd eaten many a slender meal.
Of sharp sauce, why she needed no great deal,
15 For dainty morsel never passed her throat;
Her diet well accorded with her cote.[2]
Repletion never made this woman sick;
And no wine drank she,—either white or red;
Her board was mostly garnished, white and black,
20 With milk and brown bread, whereof she'd no lack,
Broiled bacon and sometimes an egg or two,
For a small dairy business did she do.

[1]*managing*

[2]*small shed; i.e.,
her eating habits
marched her mod-
est home*

        A yard she had, enclosed all roundabout
        With pales,3 and there was a dry ditch without,
25   And in the yard a cock called Chanticleer.
     In all the land, for crowing, he'd no peer.
     His voice was merrier than the organ gay
     On Mass days, which in church begins to play;
     More regular was his crowing in his lodge

30   Than is a clock or abbey horologe.4
     And when fifteen degrees5 had been ascended,
     Then crew he so it might not be amended.
     His comb was redder than a fine coral.
     And battlemented like a castle wall.
35   His bill was black and just like jet it shone;
     This noble cock had in his governance
     Seven hens to give him pride and all pleasance,

     Which were his sisters and his paramours6
     And wondrously like him as to colours,
40   Whereof the fairest hued upon her throat
     Was called the winsome Mistress Pertelote.
     Courteous she was, discreet and debonnaire,
     Companionable, and she had been so fair
     That truly she had taken the heart to hold
45   Of Chanticleer, locked in every limb;
     He loved her so that all was well with him.
     But such a joy it was to hear them sing,
     Whenever the bright sun began to spring,
     In sweet accord, "My love walks through the land."
50   So it befell that, in a bright dawning,
     As Chanticleer 'midst wives and sisters all
     Sat on his perch, the which was in the hall,
     And next him sat the winsome Pertelote,
     This Chanticleer he groaned within his throat
55   Like man that in his dreams is troubled sore.
     And when fair Pertelote thus heard him roar,
     She was aghast and said: "O sweetheart dear,
     What ails you that you groan so? Do you hear?
     You are a sleepy herald. Fie, for shame!"
60   And he replied to her thus: "Ah, madame,
     I pray you that you take it not in grief,
     By God. I dreamed I'd come to such mischief,

Just now, my heart yet jumps with sore affright.
I dreamed, that while I wandered up and down
65 Within our yard, I saw there a strange beast
Was like a dog, and he'd have made a feast
Upon my body, and have had me dead.
His snout was small and gleaming was each eye.
Remembering how he looked, almost I die;
70 And all this caused my groaning, I confess."
     "Aha," said she, "fie on you, spiritless!
Alas!" cried she, "for by that God above,
Now have you lost my heart and all my love;
I cannot love a coward, by my faith.
75 For truly, whatsoever woman saith,
We all desire, if only it may be,
To have a husband hardy, wise, and free.
How dare you say, for shame, unto your love
That there is anything that you have feared?
80 Have you not man's heart, and yet have a beard?
Alas! And are you frightened by a vision?
Dreams are, God knows, a matter for derision.
Visions are generated by repletions
And vapours and the body's bad secretions."[7]
85   "Lo, Cato,[8] and he was a full wise man,
Said he not, we should trouble not for dreams?
Now, sir," said she, "when we fly from the beams,
For God's love go and take some laxative;
On peril of my soul, and as I live,
90 I counsel you the best, I will not lie.
Be merry, husband, for your father's kin!
Dread no more dreams. And I can say no more."
     "Madam," said he, "gramercy[9] for your lore.
Nevertheless, not running Cato down,
95 Who had for wisdom such a high renown,
And though he says to hold no dreams in dread,
By God, men have, in many old books, read
Of many a man more an authority
Who say just the reverse of his sentence,
100 And have found out by long experience
That dreams, indeed, are good significations,
As much of joys as of all tribulations

[7] *an imbalance of certain bodily fluids was supposed to cause mood disorders and bad dreams*

[8] *Roman author whose works were often cited in the medieval period*

[9] *great thanks*

That folk endure here in this life present.
There is no need to make an argument;
105 The very proof of this is shown indeed."
         "One of the greatest authors that men read
Says thus: That on a time two comrades went
On pilgrimage, and all in good intent;
And it so chanced they came into a town
110 Where there was such a crowding, up and down
Of people, and so little harbourage,
That they found not so much as one cottage
Wherein the two of them might sheltered be.
Wherefore they must, as of necessity,
115 For that one night at least, part company;
And each went to a different hostelry
And took such lodgment as to him did fall.
Now one of them was lodged within a stall,
Far in a yard, with oxen of the plow;
120 That other man found shelter fair enow,[10]
As was his luck, or was his good fortune,
Whatever 'tis that governs us, each one."
         "So it befell that, long ere it was day,
This last man dreamed in bed, as there he lay,
125 That his poor fellow did unto him call,
Saying: 'Alas! For in an ox's stall
This night shall I be murdered where I lie.
Now help me, brother dear, before I die.
Come in all haste to me. 'Twas that he said.
130 This man woke out of sleep, then, all afraid;
But when he'd wakened fully from his sleep,
He turned upon his pillow, yawning deep,
Thinking his dream was but a fantasy.
And then again, while sleeping, thus dreamed he.
135 And then a third time came a voice that said
(Or so he thought): 'Now, comrade, I am dead;
Behold my bloody wounds, so wide and deep!
Early arise tomorrow from your sleep,
And at the west gate of the town,' said he,
140 'A wagon full of dung there shall you see,
Wherein is hid my body craftily;
Do you arrest this wagon right boldly.

[10]*enough*

They killed me for what money they could gain.'
And told in every point how he'd been slain,
145 With a most pitiful face and pale of hue.
And trust me well, this dream did all come true;
For on the morrow, soon as it was day,
Unto his comrade's inn he took the way;
And when he'd come into that ox's stall
150 Upon his fellow he began to call."
    "The keeper of the place replied anon,
And said he: 'Sir, your friend is up and gone;
As soon as day broke he went out of town.'
This man, then, felt suspicion in him grown,
155 Remembering the dream that he had had,
And forth he went, no longer tarrying, sad,
Unto the west gate of the town, and found
A dung-cart on its way to dumping-ground,
And it was just the same in every wise
160 As you have heard the dead man advertise;
And with a hardy heart he then did cry
Vengeance and justice on this felony:
'My comrade has been murdered in the night,
And in this very cart lies, face upright.
165 I cry to all the officers,' said he
'That ought to keep the peace in this city.
Alas, alas, here lies my comrade slain!'"
    "Why should I longer with this tale detain?
The people rose and turned the cart to ground,
170 And in the center of the dung they found
The dead man, lately murdered in his sleep."
    "O Blessed God, Who art so true and deep!
Lo, how Thou dost turn murder out alway!
Murder will out, we see it every day.
175 Murder's so hateful and abominable
To God, Who is so just and reasonable,
That He'll not suffer that it hidden be;
Though it may skulk a year, or two, or three,
Murder will out, and I conclude thereon.
180 Immediately the rulers of that town,
They took the carter and so sore they racked
Him and the host, until their bones were cracked,

That they confessed their wickedness anon,
And hanged they both were by the neck, and soon.
185 And therefore, pretty Pertelote, my dear,
By such an old example may you hear
And learn that no man should be too reckless
Of dreams, for I can tell you, fair mistress,
That many a dream is something well to dread.
190 Upon this point I say, concluding here,
That from this vision I have cause to fear
Adversity; and I say, furthermore,
That I do set by laxatives no store,
For they are poisonous, I know it well.
195 Them I defy and love not, truth to tell."
    "But let us speak of mirth and stop all this;
For when I see the beauty of your face,
You are so rosy-red beneath each eye,
It makes my dreadful terror wholly die.
200 For when I feel at night your tender side,
I am so full of joy and all solace
That I defy, then, vision, aye and dream."
And with that word he flew down from the beam,
For it was day, and down went his hens all;
205 And with a cluck he them began to call,
For he had found some corn within the yard.
Regal he was, and fears he did discard.
He looked as if he were a grim lion
As on his toes he strutted up and-down;
210 He deigned not set his foot upon the ground.
He clucked when any grain of corn he found,
And all his wives came running at his call.
Thus regal, as prince is in his hall,
I'll now leave busy Chanticleer to feed,
215 And with events that followed I'll proceed.
    Since March began, full thirty days and two,
It fell that Chanticleer, in all his pride,
His seven wives a-walking by his side,
Cast up his two eyes toward the great bright sun.
220 "The sun, my love," he said, "has climbed anew.
My lady Pertelote, whom I adore,
Mark now these happy birds, hear how they sing.

And see all these fresh flowers, how they spring;
Full is my heart of revelry and grace."

225   But suddenly he fell in grievous case;
For ever the latter end of joy is woe.
God knows that wordly joys do swiftly go.
But now I must take up my proper theme.
          A brant[11]-fox, full of sly iniquity,

230   That in the grove had lived two years, or three,
Now by a fine premeditated plot
That same night, breaking through the hedge, had got
Into the yard where Chanticleer the fair
Was wont, and all his wives too, to repair;

235   And in a bed of greenery still he lay
Till it was past the quarter[12] of the day,
Waiting his chance on Chanticleer to fall.
O Chanticleer, accursed be that morrow
When you into that yard flew from the beams!

240   You were well warned, and fully, by your dreams
That this day should hold peril damnably.
But that which God foreknows, it needs must be.
Whether the fact of God's great foreknowing[13]
Makes it right needful that I do a thing

245   (By needful, I mean, of necessity);
Or else, if a free choice he granted me,
To do that same thing, or to do it not,
Though God foreknew before the thing was wrought;
Or if His knowing constrains never at all,

250   Save by necessity conditional.
I have no part in matters so austere;
My tale is of a cock, as you shall hear,
That took the counsel of his wife, with sorrow,
Now women's counsels oft are ill to hold;

255   A woman's counsel brought us first to woe,
And Adam caused from Paradise to go,
Wherein he was right merry and at ease.
But since I know not whom it may displease
If woman's counsel I hold up to blame,

260   Pass over, I but said it in my game.
Read authors where such matters do appear,
And what they say of women, you may hear.

[11]*brown*

[12]*i.e., it was about nine a.m.*

[13]*Chanticleer refers to a common religious debate over whether humans (or roosters) are given free will*

14an ironic state-
ment on Chaucer's
part

15an invented med-
ical authority

These are the cock's words, they are none of mine;[14]
No harm in women can I e'er divine.
265   All in the sand, a-bathing merrily,
Lay Pertelote, with all her sisters by,
There in the sun; and Chanticleer so free
Sang merrier than mermaid in the sea
(For Physiologus[15] says certainly
270 That they do sing, both well and merrily).
And so befell that, as he cast his eye
Among the herbs and on a butterfly,
He saw this fox that lay there, crouching low.
Nothing of urge was in him, then, to crow;
275 But he cried "Cock-cock-cock" and did so start
As man who has a sudden fear at heart.
For naturally a beast desires to flee
From any enemy that he may see.
    He would have fled but that the fox anon
280 Said: "Gentle sir, alas! Why be thus gone?
Are you afraid of me, who am your friend?
Now surely, I were worse than any fiend
If I should do you harm or villainy.
I came not here upon your deeds to spy;
285 But, certainly, the cause of my coming
Was only just to listen to you sing.
For truly, you have quite as fine a voice
As angels have that Heaven's choirs rejoice.
Save you, I never heard a man so sing
290 As did your father in the grey dawning;
Truly 'twas from the heart, his every song.
And that his voice might ever be more strong,
He took such pains that, with his either eye
He had to blink, so loudly would he cry,
295 A-standing on his tiptoes therewithal,
Stretching his neck till it grew long and small.
And such discretion, too, by him was shown,
There was no man in any region known
That him in song or wisdom could surpass.
300 I have well read, in Dan Burnell the Ass,[16]
Among his verses, how there was a cock,
Because a priest's son gave to him a knock

16a popular satire

Upon the leg, while young and not yet wise,
He caused the boy to lose his benefice.
305 But, truly, there is no comparison
With the great wisdom and the discretion
Your father had, or with his subtlety.
Now sing, dear sir, for holy charity,
See if you can your father counterfeit."
310   This Chanticleer his wings began to beat,
As one that could no treason there espy,
So was he ravished by this flattery.
Alas, you lords! Full many a flatterer
Is in your courts, and many a cozener,[17]   [17]*cheater*
315 That please your honours much more, by my fay,
Than he that truth and justice dares to say.
Go read the Ecclesiast[18] on flattery;   [18]*the author of the*
Beware, my lords, of all their treachery!   *book of*
This Chanticleer stood high upon his toes,   *Ecclesiastes, in*
320 Stretching his neck, and both his eyes did close,   *the Bible*
And so did crow right loudly, for the nonce;
And Russel[19] Fox, he started up at once,   [19]*typical name for*
And by the gorget[20] grabbed our Chanticleer,   *a fox in fables and*
Flung him on back, and toward the wood did steer,   *parables*
325 For there was no man who as yet pursued.
O destiny, you cannot be eschewed!   [20]*throat*
Alas, that Chanticleer flew from the beams!
Alas, his wife recked nothing of his dreams!
This simple widow and her daughters two
330 Heard these hens cry and make so great ado,
And out of doors they started on the run
And saw the fox into the grove just gone,
Bearing in his mouth the cock away.
And then they cried, "Alas, and weladay!
335 Oh, the fox!" and after him they ran,
And after them, with staves, went many a man;
Ran Coll, our dog, and Talbot and Garland,
Ran cow and calf and even the very hogs,
So were they scared by barking of the dogs
340 And shouting men and women all did make,
They all ran so they thought their hearts would break.
And now, good men, I pray you hearken all.

Behold how Fortune turns all suddenly
The hope and pride of even her enemy!
345 This cock, which now lay in the fox's mouth,
In all his fear unto the fox did clack
And say: "Sir, were I you, as I should be,
Then would I say (as God may now help me!),
'Turn back again, presumptuous peasants all!
350 A very pestilence upon you fall!
Now that I've gained here to this dark wood's side,
In spite of you this cock shall here abide.
I'll eat him, by my faith, and that anon!'"
    The fox replied: "In faith, it shall be done!"
355 And as he spoke that word, all suddenly
This cock broke from his mouth, full cleverly,
And high upon a tree he flew anon.
And when the fox saw well that he was gone,
"Alas," quoth he, "O Chanticleer, alas!
360 I have against you done a base trespass
Inasmuch as I made you afeared
When I seized you and brought you from the yard;
But, sir, I did it with no foul intent;
Come down, and I will tell you what I meant.
365 I'll tell the truth to you, God help me so!
    "Nay then," said he, "beshrew us both, you know,
But first, beshrew[21] myself, both blood and bones,
If you beguile me, having done so once,
You shall no more, with any flattery,
370 Cause me to sing and closeup either eye;
For he who shuts his eyes when he should see,
And wilfully, God let him ne'er be free!"
    "Nay," said the fox, "but God give him mischance[22]
Who is so indiscreet in governance[23]
375 He chatters when he ought to hold his peace."
    But you that hold this tale a foolery,
As but about a fox, a cock, a hen,
Yet do not miss the moral, my good men.
For Saint Paul says that all that's written well
380 Is written down some useful truth to tell.
Then take the wheat and let the chaff lie still.
    And now, good God, and if it be Thy will,

[21]*curse*

[22]*ill fortune*

[23]*self-control*

As says Lord Christ, so make us all good men
And bring us into His high bliss. Amen.

Glossary and Vocabulary

anon—soon

Aristotle—ancient Greek philosopher whose work was highly influential in the Middle Ages.

aught—any

aye—ever

Canterbury—Cathedral in the southeast of England; an important destination for Christian pilgrims because it was the location of the murder of Thomas a Becket.

Catholic Church—the center of life in medieval Europe. Churches other than the Catholic were not in existence until after 1519, when Martin Luther started the Protestant Reformation—although some groups of people within the Church did rebel against what they thought were its sinful tendencies. Chaucer himself obviously has some problems with certain trends in the Church, like the selling of indulgences (practiced by the Pardoner) and the "buying off" of Church officials (like the Summoner).

chivalry—the code of honor among knights. Idealized in literature, this code dictated that knights must be honorable, brave, and courteous to women.

churl—rude man

clergy—divided into *regular* and *secular*; regular clergy included monks and friars, while the secular clergy included local officials like the parson.

Crusades—a series of wars fought on behalf of the Christian faith. The Crusade at Alexandria (year) is mentioned in connection with the Knight.

ere—before

fain—glad, eager

fay—faith

frame story—a narrative structure in which one or more stories are contained within another story; the containing story forms a "frame"around the others. Chaucer begins the *Canterbury Tales* with a General Prologue, in which he describes the pilgrims who will each tell a story; their stories then follow, interspersed with details about what happened as they told the stories.

guilds—trade organizations for artisans and craftsmen. Like today's unions, the guilds provided economic and political power for their members; they also purchased public works and entertainment.

First Mover—in Aristotelian philosophy, God is the "first cause" of existence; he sets into motion the chain of being that human beings are a part of. Medieval religious philosophy sometimes depicted the universe as a series of circles or spheres, with Earth at the center and God as the "First Mover" at the outside.

hie—hurry

London—capital of England and center of trade and commerce. Chaucer knew the city intimately, and held positions within the court and London government.

martyr—a person who chooses to die for his or her faith.

naught—nothing

nones—occasion

Oxford—the oldest university in England.

plague—also called the Black Death; wiped out a third of Europe in the fourteenth century. Resulted in a labor shortage, since most of the good workers were killed; surviving laborers could demand more money for their services and more freedom

pilgrimage—in Chaucer's time, good Christians were supposed to make a yearly pilgrimage to a significant religious site. Some of these locations, like Canterbury Cathedral, were places where *martyrs* for the Christian faith had died.

shire—village

swink—toil

Thomas a Becket—archbishop who was assassinated by royal agents at Canterbury Cathedral and subsequently made a saint. Canterbury Cathedral was a destination for religious pilgrims because of the shrine to Thomas a Becket there.

trow—believe

three estates—the three main divisions of medieval society: clergy, aristocrats, and commoners. In the *Canterbury Tales*, the knight is supposed to be the ideal representation of the aristocratic class, while the parson and plowman are the ideal models of the clergy and laboring classes. Of course, as the Wife of Bath shows us, a person could be born in a somewhat low class and gain both wealth and prestige; the opposite might also occur.

vernacular—informal, common language as opposed to formal spoken or written language. In the period before Chaucer was born, French was the language spoke n by the courts and the upper classes; English was for commoners. Because of the war with France, though, the English gained a new sense of national unity, and the English language became more widely spoken.

wanton—carefree, reckless

wight—man

withal—with

Insightful and Reader-Friendly, Yet Affordable

Prestwick House Literary Touchstone Editions–
The Editions By Which All Others May Be Judged

Every Prestwick House Literary Touchstone Edition is enhanced with Reading Pointers for Sharper Insight to improve comprehension and provide insights that will help students recognize key themes, symbols, and plot complexities. In addition, each title includes a Glossary of the more difficult words and concepts.

For the Shakespeare titles, along with the Reading Pointers and Glossary, we include margin notes and eleven strategies to understanding the language of Shakespeare.

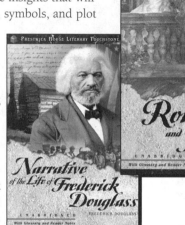

New titles are constantly being added, call or visit our website for current listing.

Special Introductory Educator's Discount – At Least 50% Off!

PRESTWICK HOUSE, INC.
"Everything for the English Classroom!"

Prestwick House, Inc. • P.O. Box 658. Clayton, DE 19938
Phone (800) 932-4593 • Fax (888) 718-9333 • www.prestwickhouse.com

SIDE 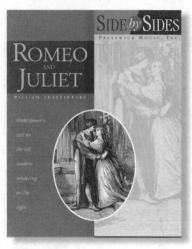 *by* SIDES